FLIP THE DECK

Integrated Composition Book for Young Students

by

TANIS KNIGHT

edited by
Theresa Zigmond

The Stack the Deck Writing Program
Tinley Park, Illinois

Acknowledgments

To Nancy Happ for her valuable comments in editing the original edition of ***Flip the Deck***, and to Penny Groves and Joe Koziarski for their illustrations.

Special thanks to Theresa Zigmond for editing this revised edition. Theresa's attention to detail, hard work, and sense of humor in completing this edition during a hectic summer made working with her a delight.

ISBN 0-933282-31-1 paperback
ISBN 0-933282-32-X hard cover

Table of Contents

3 CREATING AN INVENTION 56

4 PERSUADING YOUR AUDIENCE 80

This book is dedicated to the memory of

my parents,

who were my earliest and best teachers

Describing a Room 1

Before you begin **Chapter 1**, Tanis Knight, the author, welcomes you to a brand new learning tool--***Flip the Deck***.

Dear Student Author,

Soon you will be using this book, ***Flip the Deck***, and I want to welcome you to a year of fun and interesting writing. This book was written especially for young writers like you.

I can remember that when I was your age I often found learning to write to be confusing and boring. I decided then, that if I got the chance to teach myself, I would try to make this topic more fun and a lot easier to understand.

In ***Flip the Deck***, you will be practicing many different types of writing. You'll also learn special skills and tips which should improve your compositions right away. These new ideas will be slowly introduced, one at a time, so that you can master one technique before you move onto something else. In every chapter I made sure to build in lots of help for you--especially lots of examples and practice.

If you complete every chapter in this book, you should expect to see a big change in your writing. If you have ideas or suggestions about how to make the lessons better, I am always looking for new ideas. Write me a letter of suggestions. Then I can see your good ideas and your improved writing skills.

Good luck with ***Flip the Deck***!

Sincerely,

Tanis Knight

Tanis Knight

SCRAMBLED SENTENCES

The group of words below is really a sentence. However, the words are all mixed-up or *scrambled*. Because you have **sentence sense**, you can unscramble the words.

Scrambled Sentence: bought pink Perry Thursday on a poodle.

Sentence: *Perry bought a pink poodle on Thursday.*

You know this is a complete sentence because it is a complete thought and it makes sense. Here's another example:

Scrambled Sentence: classmates candy your with share your chocolate

Sentence: Share your chocolate candy with your classmates.

Oral Activity 1:

Unscramble the words below and turn them into complete sentences. You may use paper. All the sentences are about *bicycles.* In some groups, capital letters show the beginning of a sentence. The sentences become a little more challenging as you go along.

Example: transportation bicycles used are fun for and

Bicycles are used for fun and transportation.

1. world around bicycles are the used
2. cheap or can very bikes be expensive
3. you a imagine $10,000.00 for can paying bike ?
4. bikes many gears Some have and tires fancy
5. ridden places in can they be "off-road"
6. mountain hills can bikes go steep up
7. tires bounce rocks Their over fat bumps and
8. built light to bikes racing very are go fast
9. kids' even Today, bikes are made ways in special
10. because Some designed do expensive they're tricks bikes are to

LANGUAGE BLOCKS

Unscrambling the sentences in **Oral Activity 1** showed that you know how to build sentences. Below are some sentences all about *babies*. These sentences are grouped in columns of words. Just by using your **sentence sense** and the words in these five columns, you can build hundreds of new sentences. The first four have been completed for you.

Column 1	Column 2	Column 3	Column 4	Column 5
1. Amber	bangs	her	empty	cup.
2. Justin	bites	the	soggy	teddy bear.
3. Yolanda	hugs	only	squishy	toys.
4. Freddy	claps	two	little	hands.

Sometimes a new sentence will need an extra word, or you can change the form of a word to make it work in new ways.

Examples: bang, banging, banged
empty, emptied, empties
clap, clapping, clapped

By adding **extra words** to help connect ideas, we can also make new sentences.

Extra Words: and, but, or, before, while, by, of, who, was, after

The sentences below were made by choosing words from different columns and putting them together in different ways to make two new sentences.

5. After Amber hugs her little teddy bear, Justin bangs the squishy cup.
1 2 3 4 5 1 2 3 4 5

6. Freddy hugs Amber **and** Yolanda claps.
1 2 1 1 2

Oral Activity 2:

Now use the boxes below to build your new sentences in the same way. You can use any word which comes from a column with the same number. Remember, you can also use the extra words or change the form of the word-- *empty, empties, emptied.* **Funny sentences are great and fun to make up!**

1.	1	2	3	4	5		
2.	1	4	3	4	5		
3.	4	1	2	**and**	2	3	4
	5						
4.	1	2	1				
5.	1	2	3	4	5,	**but**	
	1	2	3	4	5.		
6.	3	5	**was**	2	by	1	
7.	**While**	1	4	3	5,		
	1	2	3	4	5		
8.	1,	**who**	2	3	5,	**was**	
	2	**by**	1.				
9.	**After**	2-**ing**	3	5,	1	4	3
	5						
10.	3	5	2	1			

Simple Sentence Combining

THE GREATEST COMPUTER IN THE WORLD

What is the greatest computer in the world? Apple? IBM? Macintosh? None of these. It's your brain. When you speak, within milli-seconds, your brain computes ideas and helps you communicate by forming sentences.

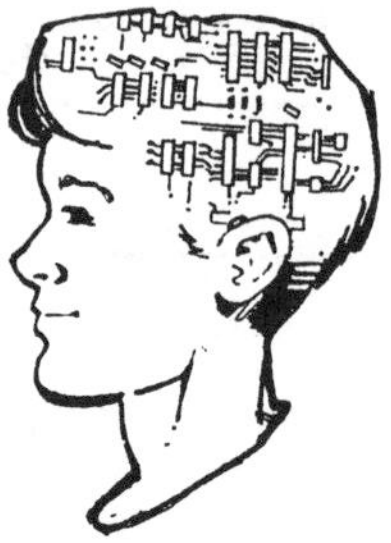

Let's prove this to you. Orally, make one sentence of these four:

There is a child.
The child is small.
There is a swimming pool.
The child jumped.

What sentence did you make? You probably said:

The small child jumped into a swimming pool. or
There is a small child who jumped into a swimming pool.

Look at the oral skills you used:

You **combined** four sentences into one.
You **rearranged** words--you probably put *small* before *child.*
You **subtracted** unnecessary words.
You **expanded**. You probably added *who* or *into.*

You automatically used these skills. They will become your **writer's vocabulary**. These writer's skills will not only help you write more interesting sentences, but will also help you revise a first draft. Wait and see.

PUTTING TOGETHER SENTENCES

Every time you say or write a sentence, you put many words together to form a new idea--**combine**. From the time you were very young, you were an expert at making up these new thoughts. For example, look at the questions that this writer had to answer to make the new sentences.

Example:

Doer? Who?	Does---Did?	What?	When? Where? Why? How?
1. The hockey player	fired	the puck	at the stunned goalie.
2. Humpty Dumpty	found	some glue	to repair his mood.

Practice 1: Every time you build a new sentence (**combine**), you ask and answer the same kinds of questions in split-second time. Use the guide words below to see how easy it is to make some new sentences of your own. Follow the sample pattern that is used in the example.

Set 1	Doer? Who?	Does?	What?
Examples:	The computer	makes	graphics.
	Bashful Bud	eats	pickles.

1. Seymour____________________________________

2. The football player______________________________

3. The tooth fairy________________________________

Set 2	Doer? Who?	Does?	What?	When?
Examples:	The rodeo star	eats	dust	every weekend.
	Grandma	makes	applesauce	in the fall.

1. ______________________________

2. ______________________________

3. ______________________________

Set 3	Doer? Who?	Does?	What?	How?
Examples:	Terrible Trixie	ate	her crayons	noisily.
	Fred	whistled	a nursery rhyme	loudly.

1. ______________________________

2. ______________________________

3. ______________________________

Set 4	Doer? Who?	Does?	What?	Where?
Examples:	The cow	scratched	its back	on the fence.
	My brother	rode	his new bike	to the dump.

1. ______________________________

2. ______________________________

3. ______________________________

Set 5	Doer? Who?	Does?	What?	Why?
	The grocery man	sprays	vegetables	to make them look better.
	The clown	blew up	balloons	to make the children laugh.

1. ______________________________

2. ______________________________

3. ______________________________

Practice 2: Now you have seen how easy it is to **combine** and **stretch** to make new sentences of your own. See if you can make more. **Expand** or **stretch** each mini-sentence below by answering the question words. Do the first two as a group activity.

Examples:	The crocodile swam.	**How?**	**Where?**
	The crocodile swam	quietly	through the swamp.
	The bandit jumped.	**Where?**	**When?**
	The bandit jumped	on his horse	after the holdup.

1. The hungry snakes ate	What?		
2. Felicia drove	Where?	When?	
3. The wonderful old woman bought	What?	Why?	
4. The chef made	What?	When?	Why?
5. The tall magician opened	What?	How?	

6. The toy came alive and zoomed — Where? Why?

7. The king's pickle-taster rushed — Where? Why? When?

8. The freckle-faced dog jumped — How? Where?

9. My Aunt Nellie made — What? When? Why?

10. The gorilla grabbed — How? When? Why? What?

Practice 3: With no trouble you have been **stretching (expanding)** your sentences to make them more interesting. Here are some more practice sentences. Answer the question words in the following sentences.

Examples:

His ______________ hat sits ______________.
(what kind of?) (where?)

His **cowboy** hat sits **on his horse's head.**

The ______________ troll giggled ______________.
(what kind of?) (why?)

The **purple** troll giggled **because the lady bug tickled him.**

The ______________________ pony ran ______________ around
(*what kind of ? *3 times) (how?)

her pasture.

The **spotted**, **friendly**, **frisky** pony ran **happily** around her pasture.

Write all your sentences together as if they were one complete paragraph.

1. George was a(an) ______________giraffe who spent the entire day
(what kind of ?)

walking ______________ through the______________.
(how?) (where?)

2. His __(1),_____(2),______(3)________neck could be seen rising over the
(*what kind of? *3 times)

______________ as he ambled along munching tasty, leaf treats.
(what?)

3. George had a good friend named Bubba. Bubba was a__________.
(what?)

4. On a __________________morning, George jogged ___________ to
(what kind of?) how?)

the swamp looking for Bubba because _______________.
(why?)

5. Bubba wasn't there, so George had to lope _____________ over to the
(how?)

___________________.
(where?)

6. Underneath the ____(1),_____(2),______(3)_____coconut tree, George
(*what kind of? *3 times)

finally found Bubba snoring _______________.
(how?)

7. "Wake up, wake up," George screeched_____________ to Bubba.
(how?)

8. George finally nipped Bubba __________________and said,
(where?)

"__________________________________."
(what?)

9. When Bubba heard George's words, he sat up_____________, grabbed
(how?)

his ___________________hat, and took George______________.
(what kind of?) (where?)

10. When last seen, the ___________ pair were galloping_________ over
(what kind of?) (how?)

the _________________pathway.
(what kind of?)

COMMAS IN A SERIES

In some of the sentences you completed earlier in this chapter, you described something using three new words or phrases. Look at sentence six (6) for example. It could have been written this way:

Sentence 6:

> Underneath the **tall, scraggly, puny-looking** coconut tree, George finally found Bubba snoring horribly.

Notice that for *coconut tree* there are three describing words or phrases: **tall, scraggly,** and **puny-looking**. Many times we realize that these words add more interest or color to sentences. You probably know that colorful words like these are called adjectives. In the sample sentence, you can see that there is a comma separating each of these words. This is because all these words are in the same *series*, and they all describe the coconut tree.

Remember this rule:

Words in a series, all describing the same thing, must be separated by a comma. There is no comma after the last adjective in the series.

Practice 4: Fill in the word blanks below to complete the rest of these sentences. Be sure to use descriptive words (**adjectives**) and include the commas.

1. The ________________, ________________, ________________wind

blew over my mother's________________, ________________

pansies.

2. Matilda didn't know that her__________________, ________________, and

______________ pie would so impress the judges at the fair.

3. The monster's______________________, ______________________, and

______________eyes were so terrifying that I couldn't move my

________________, _______________________ feet.

Practice 5: Add commas where they belong in the sentences below.

1. My smooth chocolate frozen yogurt was dripping onto the sticky dusty floor.

2. The lazy-looking bobbing blue boat was only a tiny speck on the horizon.

3. The girl with the ivory smooth clear skin had taken her black billowing hair and made it into French braids.

4. Horatio bought a delicious steaming and onion-filled hot dog with his last dollar.

5. He developed a computer program which was simple fun and easy to learn.

Practice 6: Describe the following words in sentences using two or three adjectives and separating each series of descriptive words with commas where needed. Use your series in a complete sentence.

Example: tennis shoes

The **tattered, high-top, dirty** tennis shoes were moving like lightning across the basketball court.

1. turnips
2. football player
3. camel
4. car/ road (Use both words in the same sentence.)
5. spaceship

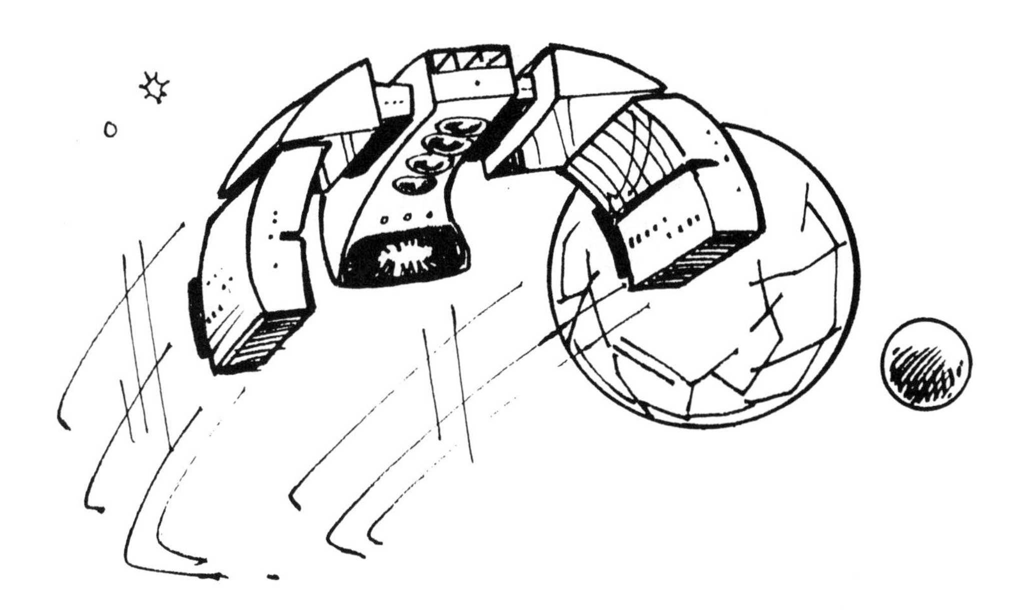

COMPARING WITH SIMILES

In just a little time you have practiced 1) **combining** and **expanding** sentences to make them more interesting and 2) **using a punctuation rule** in **expanded** sentences to help the reader. Soon you can use these new tools in your own writing.

First, let us work on one more thing to help make your composing more interesting. Sometimes writers will compare two very different things to help make a better picture in the reader's mind. The two things may be very different, but they make a good mind picture.

Examples: 1. My **undershirt** was torn and looked ***like*** **Swiss cheese**.

2. His **flattop haircut** felt ***like*** **sandpaper**.

3. The **river water** was as brown ***as*** **three-day-old dishwater**.

The writer used the words *like* or *as* to compare these things.

undershirt<---------------------->Swiss cheese

flattop haircut <------------------>sandpaper

river water<---------------------->dishwater

Even though these words are not **really** alike, when they are used together in this way with *like* or *as*, we can see a clear picture in our minds. This use of words is called writing **similes** (**sim** i lees).

Practice 7: Find the two things that are compared as **similes** in the sentences below. Also, list the word used to compare the **simile**. In the example below, this comparing word is *like.*

Example: The syrup bubbled *like* hot, sticky oil.

syrup------>**like**-----> hot, sticky oil

1. The dust rose from the ball field like a cloud of flour.
2. My backyard looks like a wet spinach salad.
3. I was as cold as a hamburger in a deep freeze.
4. The carrots in the salad looked like left over confetti.
5. The kitten's whiskers were chopped and droopy like the ragged teeth on an old toothbrush.
6. His soccer shirt was wrinkled like the skin on an elephant's leg.
7. She shook his hand which was as limp as a wet noodle.
8. The lawn mower's sound was like five hundred mosquitoes whistling *Dixie*.
9. I feel as lazy as an ant who just ate a cheeseburger.
10. Emily's purple fingernails seemed like long, grape popsicles.

Practice 8: Below are two lists of words. You can compare any of the words in **list one** to one of the words in **list two**. Use a **simile** to make your comparison and then use that simile in a sentence. Write five new sentences.

List One	List Two
hamburger	spaceship
old record	soggy cardboard
pizza	crusty mud pie
frisbee	flat tire
satellite dish	donut

Example:

Harry's **hamburgers** are so bad that they taste **like** old, flat **tires** which have been in the sun too long.

Major Writing Assignment

DESCRIPTIVE WRITING--A SPECIAL PLACE

Finally, it is time to put all the things you have been learning together in your own writing or composition. It's important for you to know what to add to make this your best work possible. Therefore, here are your **learning objectives** for this paper:

STAGE ONE: PREWRITING

Student Learning Objectives:

In this composition you will:

1. write a **short description** of a place you know well.

2. make your composition at least **two paragraphs** long.

3. **expand** some of your sentences to make them more interesting. Tell *where, when, why, how, what kind of.*

4. use 2 or 3 **similes** to make your descriptions more interesting.

5. use **commas** to separate descriptive words or adjectives found in a series.

Helpful Drills

Practice 9: Organizing Your Ideas. Most people can think of a place they know very well. For many students, this place is their bedroom. Take just a few minutes and draw a picture or map of your room. Use the handout your teacher will give you.

______________________________________'s **Room**

Put your first name here.

Doorway

1. In the space draw a map or picture of all the major things in your room. (bed, dresser, closet, bookcases, posters, etc.)

2. Draw what you would see if you were standing in the doorway.

3. If you want to make the room a different shape, you can draw your own map on a separate piece of paper.

4. Color and label the different parts of the room.

Writing Prompt

In this first writing activity, you are going to describe your bedroom using two different paragraphs.

You will want to use your drawing or map to help you remember all the different parts of your room. You can also use the following **Think Sheet** to help you organize your thoughts. Fill it out completely.

Name____

Think Sheet--My Room

1. As you look at your drawing or map, think of all the most important or noticeable things in your room. List at least 5 of these things in the first column below. When you have a list of five items, write some adjectives or phrases in the second column which best describe each item. Look at the example:

Major Things in My Room	Descriptive Adjectives or Phrases
Examples:	
goldfish bowl	bubbling, murky
bed	rumpled, pink-flowered, red bedspread
A.	
B.	
C.	
D.	
E.	

2. Now, thinking of the work you just completed in **#1**, write at least 3 sentences which describe different parts of your room. **Expand** your sentences by using plenty of colorful adjectives. Use some adjectives in a series to really dress up your work.

A. ______________________________

____

____

B. ______________________________

____

____

C. ______________________________

____

____

3. Remember that you can use similes to add style to your writing. Create your own simile to describe something in your room. List your simile (in a complete sentence) here.

____

____

____

____

____

____

____

4. In the first paragraph of your composition, you are going to describe how your room looks. What is a good opening sentence you could use to catch the reader's attention? Write a couple (2) of possible opening sentences in the spaces below:

Possibility One: ______________________________

____

____

____

Possibility Two: ______________________________

____

____

____

____

Now put a check (✔) by the sentence you think is the best way to open your paragraph.

5. In the second paragraph of your paper, you will end (conclude) by telling the reader how you feel when you are in your room. In the space below, list some of the ways you feel when you spend time in your room.

____

____

____

____

____

STAGE TWO: WRITING THE FIRST DRAFT

Now it is time to use all the information from the **Think Sheet** to write a paper about your room. You will be expected to write at least two paragraphs.

As a basic guideline, try to organize your paragraphs on your **first draft** or **sloppy copy** like this:

When you write a **sloppy copy**, it is not perfect.

- Guess how to spell hard words. Circle them to check later. Then go on. **Guess and Go**.
- Write quickly to keep your ideas flowing. Handwriting does not have to be your neatest at this time.
- Work on the story later. Not all parts must be perfect.

To make your story easier to work on later:

- Write in pencil.
- Skip every other line.
- When you finish, go back and number each sentence you wrote.

With these general guidelines in mind, you are ready to think about how you might want to organize each paragraph.

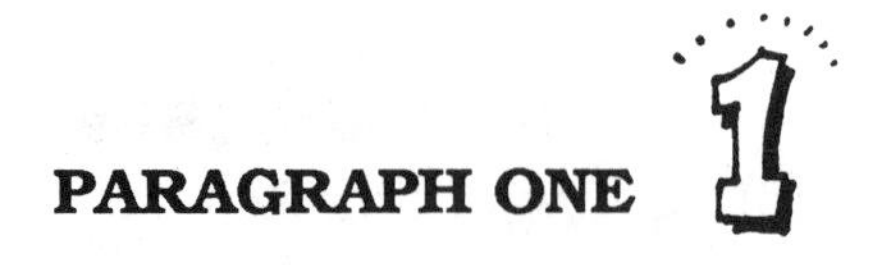

PARAGRAPH ONE 1

- Describe your room as if you were there. Tell exactly what you see as you stand in the doorway and look around. (See **Think Sheet #s1** and **2**.)

- Use your *best opening sentence* to catch the reader. (See **Think Sheet #4**.)

- Use adjectives and **expanded** sentences to make the scene clear.

- Use a simile to help with your description. (See **Think Sheet #3**.)

PARAGRAPH TWO 2

- Describe how you feel most often when you are in your room. (See **Think Sheet #5.**)

- Do not drag this paragraph on and on, but include enough information to explain what you mean.

- Use some examples.

- Use both **expanded** and shorter sentences.

- Write a good sentence to finish off the paragraph.

STAGE THREE: REWRITING

Once you have written your two paragraphs, you have completed your **rough draft** or **sloppy copy**. This means that you have two paragraphs, which are a good start. They may need some work, however, to make them ready to share with the entire class. Before you can make changes, you will need some ideas about what worked well in the paper and what will need to be changed.

On the next page is an **Editor's Checklist** to help with your rewriting tasks. A classmate or your **editing partner** will fill out this sheet after he or she reads your paper. In order to get the flow of your writing, it is OK if your partner reads your paper aloud softly. Use a *12 inch voice.* That is, you should not be able to hear the voice more than one foot away from the speaker.

Writer's Name____

Reader's Name____

Editor's Checklist

1. What did you like best about this piece of writing? Be very clear and list sentences from the paper.

2. What descriptive words or phrases helped you *see* the scene? List at least three.

3. What was the simile the writer used?

4. Did the opening sentence make you interested in reading ahead? If yes, tell why; if no, suggest some ideas to help the writer change the opening sentence.

____

____

____

____

5. What is the one thing which could most improve this paper?

____

____

____

Once you receive your **Editor's Checklist** back, you should read it carefully. Then rewrite your paper using the suggestions you think are the best. Rewrite using your very best writing. Be sure and give your paper a title.

STAGE FOUR: PUBLISHING

When you complete the final draft of your room description, you may want to draw a cover picture to finish the packet. Cut out your map or drawing and paste it on a piece of solid colored construction paper. Put your title at the top and draw a border around the picture.

Quick Review

In this first chapter you learned two **writer's vocabulary** skills--**combine** and **expand**.

If you notice that many of your sentences are short and choppy as you revise a first draft, **combine** some of them.

If your audience wants more information, you will need to **expand** by answering the questions--*who, when, where, why, how,* and *what kind of.*

Stay Tuned

In **Chapter 2** you will write about someone you know well. This *special person* will be your choice.

Writing a Character Sketch 2

In **Chapter 1** you wrote exciting sentences and paragraphs as you worked on your **writer's vocabulary** skills. This chapter will teach you even more writing tips. Let's get started!

Oral Language into Writing

PLAYING WITH NEW BEGINNINGS

It is important that young authors know that good writing takes practice. Not even very successful writers get their stories *right* the first time. Instead, they may try several different ways to write about the same thing. In this chapter, you are going to practice doing this.

Oral Activity 1:

You will need to work with a partner during this practice. Each partner has a column of items: (**Partner 1** or **Partner 2**). See the next page. Here are the directions for your columns.

1. Look at the first word(s) in your column. These words describe a place. They also describe the way this place should make a reader *feel*.

2. Think of two or three *lead in* sentences that you could use to describe the setting and feelings. These should be new sentences you create to help describe the **bold** word. Remember you will need good **adjectives** or **similes** to help you do this. Jot these sentences on a piece of scratch paper first.

Example: in front of a campfire--**peaceful**

> The night was inky black and so still that I could hear even my breath whooshing slowly in and out; in and out, like a sighing lullaby. In the velvet sky only the luminous yellow moon broke through the dark fabric of the sky.

- How does the author help you feel a **peaceful** scene?
- What special adjectives does she use?
- Are there any similes?

3. Now, look at the same word/s again. This time think of some different sentences and colorful words you could use to describe the same place and feelings. Write these sentences down also.

4. As soon as you and your partner have two (2) descriptions for the same place, take turns and read your descriptions aloud to each other. Listen to both sentences and decide which sample sounds the best (which group of sentences best makes you *feel* a certain way?) Tell your partner.

5. When one partner has finished reading, it is the other partner's turn to read. Go back and forth until each of you has written and talked about all the items in your column.

Partner 1

1. the inside of your school building at night--**scared**

2. The top of a mountain--**free**

3. in front of a campfire--**peaceful**

4. in a boat on a lake--**cold**

Partner 2

1. in a sleeping bag under the stars--**comfortable**

2. walking through a dark swamp--**creepy**

3. flying in a small plane--**terrified**

4. riding a horse--**fearless**

Oral Activity 2:

When you complete **Oral Activity 1**, you may find that one of the sentence sets was clearly your best. Use these sentences as your lead in sentences and then **expand** with more ideas into a complete paragraph. **Do not write an entire story**! Use your imagination. Just finish one paragraph which is a full description of the scene. Here are some other guidelines for this short paper.

1. Give your finished paragraph a **title**.

2. On your rough draft (or **sloppy copy**), circle any words where you are unsure of the spelling. Be sure and correct these on the final copy.

Simple Sentence Combining

GLUE WORDS

In the last chapter, you made new, interesting sentences by **expanding** the main idea. You did this by adding more information: *who? what kind of? when? where?* This is one way to **expand** sentences, but it is not the only way.

Sentences can also be stretched if the writer adds on or glues on new sentence pieces. To do this, you need to learn how to use important **glue words**.

In this book, the first type of words you will use to **combine** sentences are called **glue words**. These words *glue* ideas together.

Easy Glue Words

after	before
because	if
since	until
unless	when

Example 1:

Scott likes Wrinkles.
He's a goofy pooch.

Scott likes Wrinkles
because he's a goofy pooch.
glue word

Example 2:

Dawn doesn't go jogging.
She stretches out first.

Dawn doesn't go jogging **unless** she stretches out first.
glue word

In both the samples, these words were used to glue together two sentences. Writers use this *glue* to **combine** some sentences and make them more interesting.

Practice 1: In each set below are two short sentences. From your list, use a **glue word** to **combine** the two sentences into one. The **glue word** will be *glue* in the middle of the sentence. Underline the **glue word** you have used. Be sure to read your new sentence to see if it makes sentence sense.

Example:

I couldn't talk.
I ate too much peanut butter.

I couldn't talk **because** I ate too much peanut butter.

1. We'll eat dinner.
   Jake finishes setting the table.
   Tip: use *when*

2. Trilby could ace the test.
   She would start studying early.
   Tip: use *if*

3. The NO DRIP Paint Company puts on a basecoat.
It adds the final coat of paint.

4. Hortense had terrible heartburn.
She ate three liver and pickle pizzas.

5. The fudge delight cake dropped like a rock.
My pesty sister opened the oven door too early.

6. Peter has been very unhappy.
His teddy bear ran away.

7. Mom doesn't want to shovel the driveway.
It stops snowing.

8. Joaquin doesn't eat spaghetti.
There's lots of garlic bread to go with it.

Practice 2: In each set below, there is a pattern sentence which uses a **glue word**. Write sentences of your own which use the same **glue word**. Some of the early sentences have been started for you.

1. **Pattern:** Bears can sleep for weeks during the freezing winter **because** their heart rate slows way down.

   A. My skin looked like a burned lobster **because**____________________

   ____

   B. ____

   ____

2. The crew can't go skiing **until** we wax our skis.

A. The movie didn't get really scary **until**________________________

____

B. ____

____

3. We can go cross-country skiing **if** the snow isn't too icy.

A. The baby will stop crying **if**____________________________

____

B. ____

____

4. I can't make pickle pizza **unless** Max remembers to buy cucumbers.

A. ____

____

B. ____

____

5. Amber played soccer **after** she had finished her computer homework.

A. ____

____

B. ____

____

Practice 3: To add variety to his sentence openings, sometimes a writer will choose to use a **glue word** at the **beginning** of the sentence. Here's an example. The writer first writes two sentences like this.

Old Examples:

Mabel went ice fishing **because** she was tired of watching soap operas on TV.

My dog goes crazy **if** he sees me putting on my jogging shoes.

Since the writer wants some new sentence structures, she moves the **glue word** and the rest of the sentence to the beginning.

New Examples:

Because she was tired of watching soap operas on TV, Mabel went ice fishing.

If he sees me putting on my jogging shoes, my dog goes crazy.

> **SPECIAL ALERT!!!!!!!**
> Notice that the two parts of the sentence are separated by a **comma** when the **glue word** comes at the **beginning** of the sentence!

Expand the rest of these sentences where the **glue word** comes at the beginning of the sentence. Be sure to add the comma where it is needed.

1. **Before** the huge tree fell down,________________________.

2. **Unless** my hangnail goes away,________________________.

3. **If** you will clean out the barn,________________________.

4. **Because**________________, ________________________.

5. **Since**________________, ________________________.

6. **After**________________, ________________________.

An Easy Composing Rule

WIPING OUT SENTENCE MISTAKES--FRAGMENTS

In the last practices, you learned that **glue words** can help *glue* sentence pieces together. This helps a writer create better sentences.

Remember, though, that for the **glue word** to work, there must be **two** parts to the sentence. Each sentence part has its own subject and predicate. This shows **who** or **what** is causing the action in the sentence.

Examples:

	Part One				Part Two		
	subject	predicate		glue word	subject	predicate	
1.	We	went	bowling	**because**	it	was	too cold to play outside.
	subject	predicate		glue word	subject	predicate	
2.	I	will cry		**unless**	I	can find	frozen yogurt.
	glue word	subject	predicate		subject	predicate	
3.	**If**	we	lose	the game, (comma)	I	will feel	terrible.

Sometimes a careless writer will use a **glue word** but write only one piece of the sentence. The two pieces of the sentence are not glued together, and the piece with the **glue word** is *lonesome.*

Example: My sister Janie rolled her eyes. **Because** she was having a chocolate attack.

These two sentence pieces are written apart and are not *glued* together. *Because she was having a chocolate attack* is a lonesome sentence piece or a **sentence fragment**. Notice that this lonesome sentence fragment has been added to another sentence piece to form the complete sentence below.

New Sentence: Because she was having a chocolate attack, my sister Janie rolled her eyes.

Practice 4: In these sentences, look for **glue word** pieces which are fragments or **Frag** for short. Underline the fragment and write **Frag**. If the sentence pieces are **glued** correctly to form a complete sentence, mark **OK**. Number from 1 to 10 on your own paper and recopy each sentence. Your teacher may decide to do the first five orally.

1. The raft flipped over. After it hit the jagged rock.
2. We'll sell the computer. Unless our grandkids want to use it.
3. I cut the dog's toenails before I gave him a bath.
4. The TV blew up. When the scary show came on.
5. Audrey likes peaches because they tickle her mouth.
6. Unless you exercise often. The flab can return.
7. Until summer comes, I'll dream of summer breezes.
8. When you called. I tripped on the phone cord.
9. Before it's too late. Buy this new fishing rod.
10. We'll eat hot dogs after we parachute out of the plane.

Special Fragment Tip: On a 3 x 5 or 4 x 6 index card, write the words **I Believe That**.

I Believe That

Every time you want to see if a group of words is a fragment, pull out your card. Read the words **I Believe That** in front of the words you are checking. If the ideas make sense, it is a **sentence**. If the words sound confusing, it is probably a **fragment**.

Example: *After the game ended.*
I Believe That *after the game ended.*

Doesn't make sense, right? This is a fragment. Try this one:

We cheered after the game ended.
I Believe That *we cheered after the game ended.*

Sounds okay, right? This group of words is a sentence.

Practice 5: Now that you have practiced finding single sentence fragments, it's time for some hard detective work. It's harder to spot fragments when they come in groups or chunks of sentences. This is why it's easy to miss them when you write your own paragraphs.

In the sentence chunks which follow, see if you can find those lonesome sentence fragments. Write the number of the fragment. Then rewrite the fragment so that it is a complete sentence. You can do this by hooking the fragment to the sentence *before* or *after* the fragment piece. Or you can add your own words and make a whole new sentence. Each group of sentences has one fragment.

Alcatraz

1. Alcatraz Island, near the city of San Francisco, was a federal prison for many years. **2.** It was said to be escape proof. **3.** Because it was surrounded by water and sharks! **4.** There are no records of any criminals making it to land if they did try to escape.

5. When Alcatraz was first in use. **6.** There was a rule of silence for prisoners. **7.** Inmates were not allowed to talk. **8.** Instead, they whispered at night through the pipes in the toilets. **9.** The silence rule was lifted during later years.

10. Alcatraz Island was really a big rock with no fresh water or growing food. **11.** All the food and water had to be transported to the prison from the mainland. **12.** Since the island had no natural resources.

13. The prison was closed because it was too expensive to run. **14.** After many years of use. **15.** Many famous prisoners had spent time there, however. **16.** Al Capone, the famous gangster, was just one of these.

17. You can read more about Alcatraz and its famous history. **18.** When you're at the library. **19.** Ask the librarian to help you look up other sources. **20.** Alcatraz is a spooky but fascinating place.

CREATING A WRITTEN PICTURE

Soon it will be time to begin a new writing project. So far, you've practiced several new skills you can use for your final paper. However, the exercises that follow will give you more new ideas to help make your project outstanding.

Good writers use words and sentences to say just what they want. In the last chapter you saw how a good writer can use **adjectives** to make a clear mind picture. In this chapter, we will work on creating a certain *feeling* with words.

By doing this, you can change not only what the reader *sees* when she reads, but also what she *feels* as she reads.

Practice 6: In this activity you will be working in groups of 3 or 4. Your teacher will tell you about your group assignments. Your task is to complete a **Group Project Sheet**. You will fill this out after reading three character descriptions.

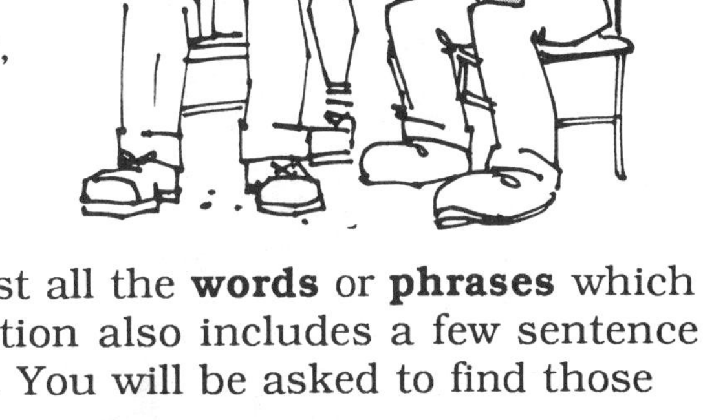

Each paragraph describes the same person in the picture. However, each character description or character sketch should create a different feeling about the person. The **Project Sheet** will ask you to label the overall **feeling** and then to list all the **words** or **phrases** which create that feeling. The third description also includes a few sentence fragments beginning with **glue words**. You will be asked to find those fragments.

Your teacher will give you more information about how to work in your group.

Character Sketch #1

Hard Driver

Dr. Sagorsky, my boss, never stops moving and doing. Usually you see his flapping coattails as he hustles down the hall, late to some meeting. Even when he's on the phone, he's pacing back and forth in front of his desk. One hand grips the phone with white knuckles. The other hand moves like a band conductor's baton as he stabs the air to make a point.

Driving home at the end of the day, I can still see his piercing stare, and I can still hear his loud voice. Even the silence seems businesslike when his memory comes to visit.

Character Sketch #2

Gitchy Goo

Doc Sagorsky scooped up his little girl and happily tickled her round tummy. Ignoring her squeals of laughter, he proceeded to trot quickly around the room playing like an airplane with his outstretched bundle. **V-A-R-O-O-M** he roared in a low, booming voice.

With a rushing swoop, he swung her over the couch, coming in wildly for a few trial landings. Finally, he bounced her onto the cushion. His eyebrows flew up and his mouth exclaimed, "Oh!"

So did the baby's. This was followed by immediate whoops and gurgles of laughter from both father and daughter. Soon they were flying off in search of another crash-landing.

Character Sketch #3

Happy Camper

D. E. Sagorsky breathed slowly and steadily as he walked along the rocky trail. Occasionally his clear eyes lazily scanned the distant fir trees. He was looking for an eagle or a hawk. Dark, tanned skin on Sagorsky's cheek bones contrasted nicely with his ice blue eyes. His muscled legs churned continuously. When he took a step forward. The pack on his back rustled softly. Sometimes his eyes crinkled and he smiled. Because he felt so rested and peaceful. Soon he was whistling softly as he headed down the trail into the twilight.

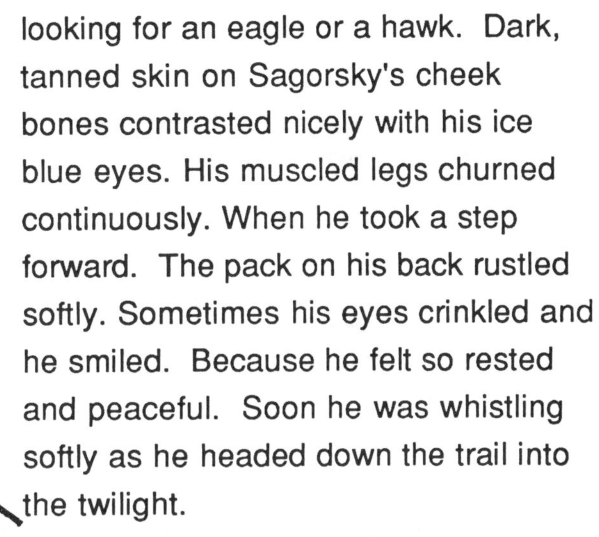

1. What's the overall feeling you have about the character in **Sketch #1**? Use two good descriptive words. The character seems:

   ____

   ____

   ____

2. What words or phrases help create the character in **Sketch #1**? Write down these words or phrases exactly as they appear in the character sketch.

   ____

   ____

   ____

3. What's the overall feeling you have about the character in **Sketch #2**? The character seems:

   ____

   ____

4. There is a simile in paragraph **#2**. Can you find it? Write it here.

   ____

5. What words or phrases helped create the character in **Sketch #2**?

   ____

   ____

6. What's the overall sense or mental picture you have about the character in **Sketch #3**? The character seems:

____

____

____

____

7. What words or phrases helped create the character in **Sketch #3**?

____

____

____

____

8. There are two sentence fragments in **Sketch #3**. What are they?

____

____

9. List the group members who worked on the project:

____

____

____

____

Practice 7: Now that your group has read several character sketches, you will create a group sketch on your own. Your group will write a paragraph describing the person in the picture. Choose a descriptive word from the list. You may want to use a word of your own. This is fine, but check with your teacher first. Describe the character to make the reader *feel* and *see* the character:

Descriptive Word List

angry
funny
calm
wild
content
excited

Your teacher will give you some more directions about how to work with your group on this assignment.

Major Writing Assignment

WRITING A CHARACTER SKETCH

Now it's time to write your own character sketch about a **favorite person you know**. This person should be someone you know *very well*. As a class, brainstorm your favorite person. How about bringing in a picture and sharing it with your classmates?

STAGE ONE: PREWRITING

Student Learning Objectives and Writing Prompt

In your paper you will:

1. write a **two** or **three paragraph** character sketch using interesting adjectives and sentences.
2. write paragraphs which make it easy to **see** your character.
3. use **similes** if needed.
4. create a **feeling** and **mental picture** about the character you are describing.
5. do not write any sentence **fragments** beginning with a **glue word**.

Here is a **Think Sheet** to help you plan for writing this sketch. Be sure to use more space and another sheet of paper if you need it.

Name____

Think Sheet--Character Sketch

1. Who are you going to describe?________________________

2. How is he/she related to you?________________________

3. List several words or phrases to tell exactly how this person looks. Be clear and list only those things which really make you *see* the person.

   ____

   ____

   ____

4. What is special about this person?________________________

   ____

5. What do you like best about this person?____________________

   ____

6. Does this person have any special sayings he/she uses?__________

   ____

   ____

7. What place (setting) do you see in your mind when you think of that person? Where would he/she spend time?

   ____

   ____

Scoring Guides

You will be graded on three areas for this paper. They are:

1. Good descriptions of a character creating a clear picture for the reader.
2. Being a careful writer.
3. Wiping out fragments.

You will earn up to 100 points in the areas above. Your teacher will use this scoring guide to grade your paper.

Character Sketch Scoring Guide

Character Description	Careful Writing	Fragments
45 points	**35 points**	**20 points**
Character is easy to see. Excellent use of adjectives. Title matches sketch. Good similes. Fun to Read.	1 or less spelling errors. Sentences begin with capitals and end with punctuation. Easy to read. Neat.	No fragments.
Sentences need more pizazz. Use more descriptive words. Title OK, but not very flashy.	2 or 3 spelling errors. Paper could be neater. Some punctuation errors.	No more than 1 FRAG.
Character hard to picture. Sentences too short. Some sentences need more information. Needs more work.	Still a sloppy copy.	More than 2 Fragments.

STAGE TWO: WRITING THE FIRST DRAFT

By using the information on your **Think Sheet**, you should be ready to write your first draft. Follow these brief guidelines:

1. Describe your character as if he/she were in the setting you chose on your **Think Sheet**. (**#7** on **page 50**.)

2. Use colorful adjectives and similes to describe how your character looks, acts, and talks.

3. Have a title for your character sketch.

4. Write at least three beginning sentences for your first paragraph. Circle the one you like best and use it as your opening sentence.

5. Write two paragraphs about your character.

6. Use similes if you want.

7. Circle any words where you are not sure of spelling. **Guess and Go**.

STAGE THREE: REWRITING

Once your rough draft or **sloppy copy** is finished, you will want to make changes before you finish your final copy. You will probably want to change ideas, but you may also want to correct fragments and incorrect spelling, and improve handwriting.

Practice 8: First Things First. When you begin to look at your rough draft, you may first want to look for simple errors or things you liked. Practice with the sample below.

1. Draw a box around any colorful words you like.
2. Underline any fragment and mark *Frag*.
3. Circle any spelling errors.

Grammy

My grandma was a ranch hand, a mother and a bizness woman. Most of all, though she wuz a lady. Grammy was tall like a beautiful queen. If she worked in the fields. She still looked crisp and clean and calm.

I loved her light blue eyes that crinkled when she smiled. Her hare wuz always pulled straight back into a coiled bun. Little hairs wood escape though. Because she worked over a hot stove. These bright red hairs circled her face in a strawberry halo.

When Grandpa died. Grammy ran the ranch by herself. She drove a tractar, but still found time to cut pretty flowers for dinner parties. I guess you cud say she was tuff and tender. I miss her alot.

Practice 9: You've had some time to practice on a sample paper. Now it's time to work on the real thing. Your teacher will assign you a revision and editing partner. First, it's time for read aloud checks with your partner. Take turns reading your papers aloud. After you have heard your partner's paper, fill out the **Listener's Checklist Sheet**.

Next, trade papers and mark the same things you marked in **Practice 7** on page **48**. Sign your name on the bottom of your classmate's paper once your proofreading is carefully finished.

Name________________________________

Listener's Checklist

1. What did you like best about this paper?

2. Use two or three words to describe the character you heard about.

3. How do you think the writer feels about the character? Why?

4. What words or phrases stick in your mind from what you heard?

Write your final draft after you have made changes based on your **Listener's Checklist** and proofreading.

STEP FOUR: PUBLISHING

Once your final draft is completed, it is time to make a nice booklet. Make a cover page for your sketch using a real photo (or drawing if no photo is available) of the person in your character sketch. Display these booklets at an open house or share them by reading aloud.

Skills Review

In this chapter you learned how to use **glue words** to **combine** sentences.

As you begin to revise a first draft--**sloppy copy**--check for the following:

- If your sentences begin with the same sentence beginning, try **combining** and/or **rearranging**.
- If you have almost the same number of words in each of your sentences, you need to vary your sentence lengths. Try **combining**.

Stay Tuned

Next you will be using your imagination and inventing a new super skateboard. You might want to sell your idea to *Toys R Us*!

Creating an Invention 3

You have finished only two chapters in this book, and already you can see your writing improve. The more you practice, the more your writing will flow. So let's get started with **Chapter 3**.

Oral Language into Writing

LANGUAGE WAREHOUSE

When you write, it's nice to have a supply of interesting words to use in your sentences. A writer almost needs a word bank or a word warehouse where he or she can store these special words. Sometimes you may want to make a deposit to the word bank as a prewriting exercise. Here are some ideas.

Oral Activity 1:

Below are some words written in **bold**. In the examples, see how many other words have been listed under each **bold** word. These words have a similar meaning to the original word. Different words which have a similar or related meaning are called **synonyms** (**sin**-o-nims).

Example:

walk	fast
stroll	quick
amble	speedy
strut	hurried
shuffle	rapid
step	

See if you can think of at least two words which are similar to the words below. Write the word and the new synonyms on your own paper.

1. pretty	**5.** nice
2. run	**6.** happy
3. horrible	**7.** mean
4. good	**8.** said

Oral Activity 2:

Often writers use **synonyms** to make their writing more exciting. They don't use the same, old, tired words over and over. Instead, they go to a word warehouse or a **thesaurus** (thi **sor** us) to find fresh words. In the sentences on the next page, think of a synonym to use in place of the **bold** word. Try to use a **synonym** which makes a better picture in the reader's mind.

Example: **Old** -- I woke up when the baby began to **cry**.

New -- I woke up when the baby began to **howl**.

Write the new sentence on your own paper and underline the synonym you used to replace the **bold** word.

1. The snake **moved** across the grass.

2. The witch **looked** at me and shook her **old** broomstick.

3. The spy **said softly**, "Get out now!"

4. The **cold** lake was **blue** under white clouds.

5. The small jet **flew** through the air like a flashing bullet.

6. The **sad** basset hound found his tummy stuck on the curb.

7. The **big** building **fell** after the dynamite explosion.

8. The **slippery** fish **slid** out of my hands.

Oral Activity 3:

By now you have the idea that synonyms can help jazz up your writing. By choosing just the right word, a writer creates sentences which are interesting to read.

Use a synonym in place of each word below. Build an exciting sentence around your new word.

1. scared or scary
2. big
3. ugly
4. boring
5. loud

Simple Sentence Combining

CONNECTORS

In earlier chapters you used your **writer's vocabulary** skills and learned how to write **expanded** sentences and to **combine** sentences with **glue words**. Now it's time to learn a new **combining** trick that's even easier to use.

Even as a little child you used **glue words** to make all sorts of new sentences. These **glue words** or **connector words** are *and*, *but*, and *or*.

See how this *glue* can be used to stretch two sentences into a new sentence.

Examples:

1. I hate turnips.
2. I think my dog would, too.

I hate turnips, **and** I think my dog would, too.

1. I wanted that new skateboard.
2. My allowance wouldn't stretch that far.

I wanted that new skateboard, **but** my allowance wouldn't stretch that far.

1. Can we go to the children's museum?
2. Is it closed?

Can we go to the children's museum, **or** is it closed?

Many times a writer will want to use a longer sentence (**expanded sentence**) to make her sentences more interesting. This way there are some longer sentences as well as short ones in a paper. Not all the sentences are short and choppy. You can use a **connector** or **glue word** to write longer compound sentences.

> Remember, a compound sentence is two complete sentences joined together by a comma and a connector glue word.

Example:

	Subject	Predicate		Comma	Connector Glue Word	Subject	Predicate	
The shaved	poodle	was	cold	,	and	she	looked	silly.
sentence one						**sentence two**		

Each sentence on each side of the **connector word** must have its own subject and predicate.

Practice 1: Combine each sentence pair using a **connector word**--*and, but,* or *or*. You may only use *and* four times. Do the first two with your whole class.

Example:

I like hot dogs.
They can even have tons of onions on top.

I like hot dogs, **and** they can even have tons of onions on top.

1. Anna Rose puffed a giant bubble.
   It blew up in her face.

2. Boston's Freedom Trail is terrific.
   Wear a pair of comfortable shoes.

3. Tarzan has to lose some weight.
   His swinging vine will snap.

4. She's my best friend.
   Sometimes we still argue.

5. Don't overuse compound sentences.
   The reader will get sick of them.

6. We went to a Lakers' game.
   They blew out the other team.

7. I took a long nap.
   My head was still pounding.

8. Many cities light their buildings at night.
   It's beautiful.

9. Aunt Matilda would always listen to me.
   I loved her weird sense of humor.

10. Do your exercises.
    You'll feel like a slug!

Practice 2: Expand each of the sentences below to make a new compound sentence. Make sure each sentence makes sense.

1. I ate the whole loaf of bread, **and** ______________________________.

2. I either want to travel to Glacier National Park, **or** ____________.

3. She gave me this gorilla, **but** ____.

4. Hand me the life jacket, **or** ____.

5. We scooted to the edge of the raft, **but** ____________________________.

6. I threw on my football jersey, **and** ______________________________.

7. ______________________________, **and** I just about fell out of my chair.

8. ______________________________ , **but** the crazy thing just yawned.

9. ______________________________, **or** the whole plan may not work.

10. ____ , **or** it will melt.

Practice 3: Below are many sentences in a complete paragraph. Left as they are, there are too many short, choppy sentences which make the paragraph hard to read. Use *and*, *but*, and *or* as glue to make *three* new sentences. Put a star next to these. Leave the rest as is.

Hilarious Hortense

My sister Hortense is an odd duck. I never know what to expect. She's unpredictable. For example, she loves the soaps and pro wrestling. She's also crazy about classical music. Hortense is 24. It's hard to tell her age. This may be due to her total look. The "Hort" may wear overalls one day. She might wear a very old-fashioned suit. Her hair is like Shirley Temple's. It's green. Yes, Hortense is on the unusual side. I love her anyway. It's terrific when she invites me to come over for beet-flavored frozen yogurt.

An Easy Composing Rule

PUNCTUATING WITH CONNECTORS

Before we leave compound sentences, there's a simple comma rule to talk about. Look at the compound sentence below.

subject	predicate		comma	connector	subject	predicate	
Growler	ate	Mom's shower cap	,	but	he	felt	fine.
sentence one					**sentence two**		

Remember that a compound sentence is two complete sentences joined by a comma and a connector word. There must be a subject and a predicate on **both sides of** the connector glue.

> In a compound sentence, a comma must come *right before* the connector word.

Practice 4: Put in the comma in the compound sentences below. Three of the sentences are not compound sentences. They will not need any comma. **#7** is tricky. Read it very carefully!

1. Jamella shot some hoops but then she did her homework.
2. The teddy bear's eyes seemed to wink.
3. It was raining cats and dogs.
4. We ate the chili and our mouths were on fire!
5. The skater did an incredible triple jump and she landed perfectly.
6. Sam had to practice or he couldn't have played goalie for the team.
7. The butcher ground the beef and stamped some packages.

8. Apply this Bug Zapper Cream or the mosquitoes will eat you alive.

9. I've always wanted to paint but my taste is in my toes.

10. I fell asleep and I dreamed about leaping lizards.

Practice 5: Read the following paragraph and find the three compound sentences. Recopy those sentences and insert the comma where it's needed.

Russian Big Top

1. The Russian circus is a wonderful thing. **2.** There are circus arenas in many Russian cities and all the citizens are big fans. **3.** Russian circus people are big stars like sports heroes in our country. **4.** Some circus people join the circus on their own but most performers come from famous circus families. **5.** These families teach circus skills to their children at a very early age.

6. A Russian circus star is paid very well. **7.** The work is hard, however. **8.** The best performers attend a special circus school in Moscow. **9.** They may work on clowning or they might practice acrobatics. **10.** Graduation from the school can mean an exciting career. **11.** Watch for the Russian circus on TV sometime. **12.** You'll see a great show!

JAZZING UP YOUR WRITING WITH SOUND

Soon it will be time to create another writing project. Here's a quick skill drill which will help with that assignment.

Read the descriptions below and as a class decide what is the same about each group of words.

Examples:

There was a **great, green, grumpy grizzly!**

With **silent sound the snake slid** closer.

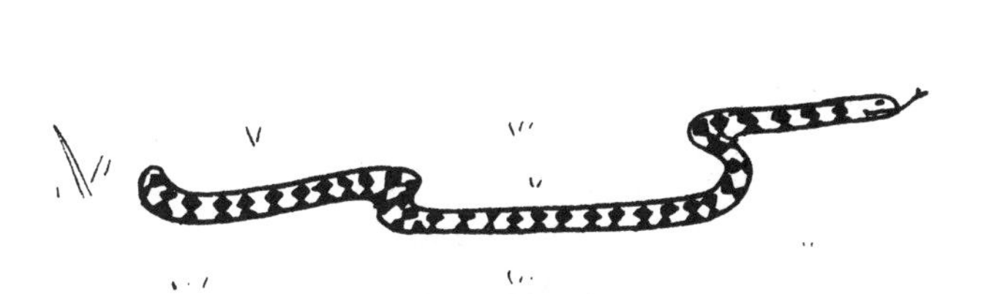

Have you practiced that old tongue twister: **rubber, baby, buggy bumpers**?

ALLITERATION

In each sentence above, the writer chose to repeat the **same letter sound** over and over in a row. When this is done in just the right spot, it can create interest and add interest in your writing. It says to the reader, "Hey, pay attention to this!" This writing style is called **alliteration** (a lit e **ray** shon). It's fun to use, but only a little at a time.

Practice 6: Add some similar sound words to the spaces below. Do the first one or two as a class. The sound to repeat is marked by a **bold** letter.

1. Henry can't find his **s**ix, **s**___________ **s**ocks.

2. **B**ig, **b**_______, **b**__________Bubba was the first to arrive.

3. We gave a **g**ift of **g**rinning, **g**_____, **g**_______ **g**old fish.

4. **L**anette can't find her **l**_________, **l**_________ **l**ady bugs.

5. Down the stretch, the snails **st**uttered, **s**_________**ed**, and **s**_________**ed** to the finish line.

6. **P**aula picked up a **p**ale, **p**___________, **p**__________sea shell.

7. That crazy dog, Jasper was **j**ump**ing** and **j**_________**ing** on its leash.

8. We could all hear the **r**_________, **r**_________, **r**_________wind.

9. The class **m**_______the butter, **m**______the popcorn and **m**__________ on it through the movie.

10. **S**_______, **s**_______Sally hit the banana peel and **s**________and **s**________all the way down the hall.

Practice 7: Write a short paragraph about Henry the Horse, Angie the Alligator or some interesting animal of your own choice. Somewhere in your paragraph use three (3) different alliterations. <u>Underline</u> these. Your paragraph can be no longer than ten sentences. Many of the paragraphs will be read aloud to the class.

Major Writing Assignment

DESCRIBING AN INVENTION

Once again it's time to create a new writing piece. Now you have even more ideas to use. In this composition you are going to describe a fun, new invention.

STAGE ONE: PREWRITING

Student Learning Objectives

In your paper you will:

1. describe a **new invention** so that someone would be able to clearly understand it and want to buy it.

2. use **similes**, **synonyms**, or **alliteration** to make your language more colorful.

3. avoid using any sentence **fragments**.

4. use **connector words** to **expand** some sentences into compound sentences.

Writing Prompt

For this assignment, you are going to describe a wacky invention (*a special skateboard*) which could be used at the North Pole. Since this sounds crazy at first, you may need some help from your friends to brainstorm ideas. Fill in a copy of the group work sheet on the next page.

WACKY INVENTION--Team Project Sheet

Your Group: You will be working with a team of three or four classmates. Members of your group are:

____

____

____

____

Task One: Your group will need to brainstorm some special features for this skateboard. Be **wild**; be **creative** because anything goes in this assignment. Nothing is too far out!

First--List all the additions (changes) to the skateboard which would make it work better in snow and ice. Anything is OK!

____

____

____

____

Task Two: Now think of ideas to make the skateboard more comfortable and easier for the rider to use. List those ideas here.

____

____

____

____

Task Three: Finally, what additions or changes could make this zany skateboard super, sharp-looking? Be creative!

____

____

____

____

____

Task Four: Your last task as a group is to draw a model of your new skateboard. Choose the best ideas from your lists above. Do your picture on the big piece of paper your teacher gives you. Label all key parts of your skateboard and be ready to explain your design to the entire class. Make sure everyone shares in the illustration. Use lots of colors and labels on your poster!

Think Sheet

Now that your group helped get you started, it's time to use the group's ideas or your own in your writing. You are going to create a written description of the skateboard using your own most colorful language. Here's a **Think Sheet** to help you polish your thoughts.

Name____

Think Sheet--Super, Sizzling Skateboard

1. What do you think are the best features of this new skateboard?

____

2. Are there any other ideas you want to add or change from the group invention?

____

3. Think of two similes you could use in your final description. They can be about the skateboard itself or about the cold environment where the skateboard is used.

   Examples: The snowdrift in front of my board is *like a cotton candy cloud.*
   My board's built in handwarmer was glowing *like a friendly, red lighthouse.*

   Simile One____________________________________

   ____

   Simile Two____________________________________

   ____

4. Next, write two descriptive phrases for your paper which use alliteration. These phrases can describe the skateboard, the North Pole, the driver, or the skateboard moving across the ice and snow. Make them fun to read!

   Phrase One____________________________________

   ____

   Phrase Two____________________________________

   ____

5. In this paper you will want to use exciting words. To help the reader really see what you are describing, brainstorm some nifty words you might use to. Come up with at least three new words or phrases to explain each bold word.

Show how the board **moves**:

____

____

____

____

Describe how the skateboard **looks**:

____

____

____

____

Describe the **North Pole environment**:

____

____

____

____

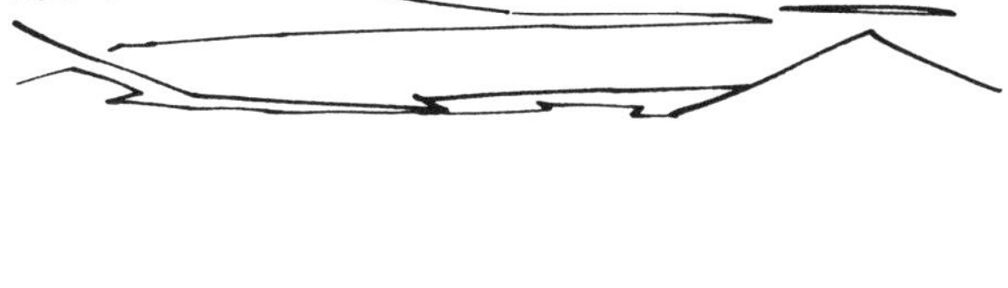

6. How will you make the reader want to buy this skateboard? List some ideas here.

____

____

____

____

____

7. This description will need to be at least three paragraphs long. Each paragraph should have its own main idea or topic. Decide which main topic you will write about in each paragraph and list those topics below.

Examples: (special features, the North Pole, how the skateboard moves, appearance, special uses, why everyone needs one)

Paragraph One_______________________________________

Paragraph Two_______________________________________

Paragraph Three_____________________________________

STAGE TWO: WRITING THE FIRST DRAFT

By using the information on your **Think Sheet**, you should be ready to write your first draft. Remember that this composition will be a description of your new skateboard.

Here are some tips to remember.

1. Make your descriptions easy to picture.
2. Describe the special movement, comfort, and appearance features of the skateboard.
3. Write at least three paragraphs. Have one main idea for each paragraph.
4. Use at least one simile and one alliteration in your paper.
5. Write using at least 3 compound sentences.
6. Write this description as if you were trying to sell the skateboard to yourself.

STAGE THREE: REWRITING

To help you rewrite your paper, you will work with a group of three or four.

First--	Each person will read her piece aloud (**quietly**) to the other members of the group.
Second--	Each person in the group will then read each paper silently and fill out an **Editor's Checklist** for each of the papers in the group. Your teacher will give you extra copies. Staple a checklist to the back of each paper after you read it and pass the packet on to the next reader.
Finally--	Each writer will receive his own paper back with two or three finished checklists.

Writer's Name______________________________ **Date**__________

Editor's Name____

Invention Checklist

(Please circle a score for each section based on your real feelings about this paper. Add extra written comments to explain your feelings.)

1. USE OF DESCRIPTIVE LANGUAGE

Blah	**OK**	**Wow!**
Too many boring words.	Some interesting words and phrases.	Great adjectives. Good similes. Fun alliteration.

1 2 3 4 5 6 7 8 9 10

Words or phrases you really liked______________________________

____

____

2. CREATIVITY

More imagination	**Average**	**Oh, Boy!**
I know you can do better than this. Way too ordinary.	Some good ideas--needs more.	Great imagination. Fun to read your ideas. Lots of extras. Wish I had thought of these.

1 2 3 4 5 6 7 8 9 10

Mention some parts you really liked.____________________________

____

3. ORGANIZATION

Too Confusing	**Pretty Good**	**A Snap to Read**
Hard to follow. No clear flow.	Some jumping around.	Each paragraph a separate topic; easy to follow. Very well organized.

1 2 3 4 5 6 7 8 9 10

Suggestions____

____

4. SENTENCE STRUCTURE

Try Again

Many fragments.
All sentences are the same length.
Few, if any compound sentences.

So-So

One fragment or not enough sentence interest. Few compound sentences.

Superstar!

No fragments.
Three compound sentences--all with commas.

1 2 3 4 5 6 7 8 9 10

Suggestion____

____

5. OVERALL IMPRESSION

Back to the Drawing Board

OK

Love It!

1 2 3 4 5 6 7 8 9 10

Comments____

Revising Your Draft After Reading the Checklists

Read all the checklists for your paper. If necessary, talk quietly about some of the comments with members in your group or a partner to explain your ideas.

When you're finished, decide on **three things** you will change or improve in your final draft. At the top of your final copy, list these three things by writing:

Example: In this paper I will improve my writing by:

1. writing no fragments

or

2. using another good simile in paragraph one

or

3. making sure that each paragraph has a separate topic.

STAGE FOUR: PUBLISHING

The best way to share your terrific skateboard pitch is by reading it aloud to your classmates. Be ready by having all these things finished:

- Your final draft.
- Completed checklists.
- Rough draft.
- A special drawing (or diagram) of your invention. It can be modeled after the group drawing or can be new. Make it big and colorful!

Share your completed paper and illustration in a new group. Choose one story to read aloud to the entire class.

Vote for the winning skateboard or the illustration which most closely follows the description. Select the favorite one from your class and send it to **The Stack the Deck Writing Program** publisher.

Stay Tuned

In your next assignment you will write a letter to your teacher or principal about . . . Guess what it is? You'll also learn about a great revising strategy.

Persuading Your Audience 4

This chapter will help you practice composition skills which you can use on a day to day basis. For example, have you ever needed to convince somebody of something? Sometimes the best way to do this is in writing.

Oral Language into Writing

SUPPORTING YOUR IDEAS

Oral Activity 1:

There are three mini-stories or **situations** (sich oo **ay** shons) for you to read in this exercise. After you read each paragraph:

- decide what you would do if you were the person in the story;
- list four good **reasons** why you would do what you said and
- write your decision and reasons in a short paragraph.

Situation 1

You and your sister are walking in the backyard one day, and you find a young hawk with a broken wing. With your Dad's help, you take the hawk to a vet. She manages to set the wing with a splint. You and your sister spend weeks nursing the bird back to health, finding just the right food, and building a special cage. You also pool your allowances to pay the vet bills. While the bird is getting better, all your friends come by to see the great, new pet you have. The two of you are almost famous in the neighborhood and at school because of Howard the Hawk.

Finally, after two months, the vet says that Howard is healed and could be set free to live in the wild if you want. What would you do and why?

Situation 2

Your birthday is in two days. Your brother tells you that your mom has spent many days shopping for just the right present. He says that she has gone to eight different stores and made a bunch of phone calls to track down what you want. You're pretty sure that she must have gotten you the bicycle helmet you had asked for.

In the afternoon, you're in the garage looking for your old tennis racket when you accidentally open a box with your present inside. It is the **wrong** helmet, even though the name of the helmet is close to the one you wanted. You realize your mom was confused and bought the other one by mistake. However, you realize she spent days tracking this one down! What would you do and why?

Situation 3

During the summer you have washed cars and mowed fifty lawns in order to earn money to buy school clothes in the fall. In September, you and your friend rush to the mall where you buy the hottest new fashions for back to school. This includes a great leather jacket which uses up a lot of your money.

When you get home and show the clothes to your mom, she is very unhappy. She thinks some of the clothes are too wild looking for school. She is also not sure that they will last. She also thinks the leather jacket costs too much. Your mom is not mad, just concerned about the choices you made. What would you tell her and why?

Simple Sentence Combining

TIME FOR REVIEW

Before moving on to practical letter writing, it's probably a good idea to review some of the **writer's vocabulary** skills you've learned in past chapters. This review will be easy.

Practice 1: The following paragraph has good information, but the sentences can drive a reader crazy because they are all short and choppy. Use your **writer's vocabulary** skill and **combine** some of the sentence bits. You can **combine** with:

Glue Words (See **page 34**.)
Adjectives and Adverbs
Items in a Series (See **page 13**.)
Connector Words (*and, but, or* -- See **page 59**.)

For each of the categories above, write at least two sentences in your new paragraph which use that same sentence pattern. You will probably be able to write a lot more! Rewrite the paragraph in your own words and on your own paper. Read it aloud to yourself to be sure it sounds the way you want.

Soccer Shocker

1. There was a soccer goalie at Egghead Elementary. **2.** The goalie's name was Shelly. **3.** Shelly was tall. **4.** Shelly was skinny. **5.** Shelly was in the fourth grade. **6.** Her legs were like toothpicks, and she was slow. **7.** Balls whizzed past those legs and into the goal. **8.** Shelly's team was the Soccer Sirens. **9.** The Sirens had the worst record in the league. **10.** They had lost every game but one. **11.** Shelly felt terrible. **12.** Her teammates couldn't seem to score any goals. **13.** Shelly couldn't stop any. **14.** Things were grim.

15. However, the girls were tough. **16.** The girls were fighters. **17.** The girls were not ready to quit. **18.** They could go to soccer camp. **19.** They needed to raise big bucks. (**Hint**: use **glue word** *if*) **20.** The team held bake sales. **21.** The team held car washes. **22.** The team held raffles. **23.** They made their goal. **24.** They went off to soccer camp. **25.** What a workout it was!

26. The girls learned nutrition. **27.** The girls did daily aerobics. **28.** They also practiced with drills, drills, and more drills. **29.** At first the puny Sirens were tired. **30.** They didn't quit. **31.** All the spikers worked hard. **32.** They started to score some goals. **33.** Shelly also got stronger. **34.** Shelly got quicker. **35.** She smothered many shots on goal. **36.** Teammates called her Shelly the Shield. **37.** Nothing got past her.

38. During the next soccer season, the Sirens were tough. **39.** They played for the league championship. **40.** They got respect from others. **41.** They respected themselves more.

An Easy Composing Rule

SKILLS REVIEW

Practice 2: Read the letter below and then use the **Writing Record Sheet** on the next two pages to think about the sentences you have read. This exercise will help you prepare for the next writing activity.

446 E. Dead Wood Road
Bliss, Idaho 82451
October 4 1991

Ms. Blabbie Adams
Heartsick Horrors Column
Seattle Sun
2899 Pike Street
Seattle WA 98556

Dear Ms. Adams:

1. I am writing to comment on a recent letter you published from a man identified as *CRANKY* in Buffalo, New York. **2.** This whiney cretin had written you to complain about his wife because she made to many boring meat loaf dinners. **3.** He also whimpered that too many times all his clothes weren't ironed before he sat down for his breakfast in the morning. **4.** His whiney, babyish, and sniveling letter asked you for help. **5.** He felt that his wife should pay more attention to him than to her job as a lawyer or to there four kids.

6. Because I really enjoy reading your column I was upset by your advice. **7.** You suggested that the numskull try to share his problems with his wife, and you also said the twerp could buy his wife a new cookbook. **8.** Give me a break! **9.** Why didn't you suggest that he learn to cook himself and help out in other ways to. **10.** Why should the guy be pampered when its clear that all the household chores are a second job only for his wife?

11. Blabby, I hope you'll read this letter and decide to write some new advice. **12.** I know you'll have some new ideas the second time around.

Sincerely,
Bertha Quagmire
Bertha Quagmire

Writing Record Sheet

Directions: Answer the questions below about the letter you just read. You can use the numbers to talk about separate sentences. Sometimes you will need to list words directly from the letter.

QUESTIONS	ANSWERS HERE
1. There are two **punctuation mistakes** in the date and inside address of the letter. What are they?	
2. Which sentence is an **expanded sentence** which begins with a **glue word**?	
3. What is the **punctuation mistake** in the same sentence?	
4. Which sentence (or sentences) uses **connector words** to join two complete sentences? What is the connector word/s?	
5. Which word is used **incorrectly** in sentence 2?	

QUESTIONS	ANSWERS HERE
6. Which sentence uses **three adjectives** in a series?	
7. What is the **punctuation error** in sentence 9?	
8. What word is used **incorrectly** in sentence 5?	
9. What word is used **incorrectly** in sentence 10?	
10. List at least four words the author uses which show how she **feels** about the man she describes. Do these words help with her purpose? Why or why not?	
11. What **punctuation mark** is always used after the greeting of a business letter?	
12. What is the **punctuation error** in sentence 6?	

WRITING FOR AN AUDIENCE

Authors write for many reasons. Sometimes they write to explain or tell you more about a topic (expository writing). Other times a writer may want to make a reader enjoy a story (narrative writing) or laugh about something. Quite often, however, adult writers compose because they need to convince the reader or readers that their opinions are the best. This is called **persuasive** (per **sway** siv) **writing**.

It's hard to be a good **persuasive writer** unless you know who will read what you write. The readers are your **audience**. Skillful writers must decide what ideas or arguments will be most persuasive or convincing by their audiences.

Practice 3: For each set of examples, you are told **who the writer** is, **who the audience** is and **what the writer** is trying to do. Read each example and decide which set of sentences convinces the audience and matches the purpose.

Working with a partner, list your choice and give at least three reasons that support your choice. Back up your reasons with actual words from the examples. Tell why the other examples were not chosen. Write your answers in complete sentences.

Writer: Fourth grade boy
Audience: His teacher
Purpose: To get more time to do an assignment

Sample Sentences #1

". . . gee, I need more time for that map thing we did. I had such a good time at Dissey Land. With Goofy and Mickey and riding on that reel scary space mountain ride. Have you ever been their with your little kid? Maybe you don't go in for that sort of thing. Teachers are like that. Anyway, I was too bizzy at D.L. and I didn't even remember to bring any of the pencils and junk we needed for the map. I could throw something together pretty fast if I had the rest of this week. Let me no soon. OK?"

Sample Sentences #2

". . . Mrs. Anderson, I know that this map assignment was very important in our social studies unit. For that reason, I would like some addishunal time to do the best job I can. Last week, my parents decided to take our entire family to Disney land at the last minute. We were all very excited. In all the rush, I managed to forget the special colored pencils we needed for the assignment. It was a stupid mistake, and I worried about it the whole time I was in California.

I realize that this is a special request, but I hope you can look at my past grade record when you make your decision. I'll certainly understand if you say that I must stick to the first time schedule. However, I know I can do a terrific job if you allow a few more days. Geography is a favorite topic of mine, and I'd like to learn more about the map of Washington State. Thanks for your time."

Sample Sentences #3

". . . and so you see, Mrs. Anderson, that chance to bond with my parents and siblings during our recent trip to the Disney Theme Park was uppermost in my mind. I took advantage of their lovely company and the wonderful scenery. Studies took a back seat to this time for relationships. When my mother requested advance permission for this trip, I think my entire family felt that dreary school work could be shoved aside for once. In the spirit of Disney Land, I think you'll agree that this *MICKEY MOUSE* type of assignment is not that big a deal. I know with a little extra time I can get something satisfactory into you. My parents and I await your response.

Writer:	Ten-year-old girl
Audience:	Her best friend
Purpose:	To explain why the writer got upset over a ruined sweater

Sample Sentences #1

". . . boy, I'm so mad. That sweater was so neat. I shopped for two whole days at the mall to find just the right color that would go with my pink parachute pants. And now there's grape juice all over the front. You didn't even ask to use it. And besides, I think that wearing it with that green skirt of yours was the worst! Those colors never looked very good on you. Your light green shirt we bought at H. J. SLICK was far better than the sweater. It's also more slimming. At least dry clean the sweater, and it will help. I'm really bummed out. Let's never trade stuff again. OK?"

Sample Sentences #2

". . . Dawn, what can i say, your a jerk sort of. My pink swetter looks yukky with that dumb grape juice. I traded with you and heres what I get, oh man. Wen I leeve stuff at yur house I never no if your brothers and sisters will bother it. I should think agin. . . because I reely loved that sweater, it had just the right color for my pants and i saved lots for it, i feal like you let me down. But yur still my friend I gess, just hurry up and get the swetter cleaned, i want to wear it skating preety soon. Can you come over for pizza after the skating party? Wear yer own clothes, ha ha.

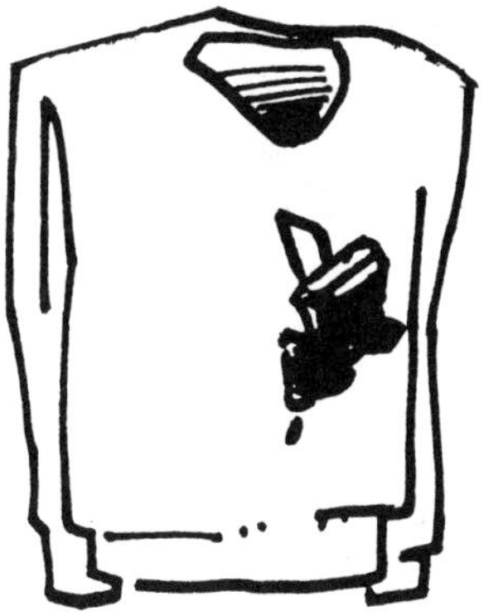

Sample Sentences #3

". . . Dawn, I hope you understand why I felt so bad about what happened to my sweater. I was very proud of that sweater because I had looked so hard to find just the right color to go with a certain pair of pants. I know it's not right to be so uptight about a piece of clothing, but I guess I had a lot invested in the sweater. Also, when I saw you at Terri's party I was very surprised to see that you had the sweater on. I know I had forgotten and left it at your house. However, you didn't ask me if you could wear the sweater to the party. Because we're friends, I probably could have let that slide. But, when I saw you spill the grape juice all down the front, I really went off the deep end and said a lot of things I shouldn't have. Now that everything is out in the open, though, I hope we can get over this. It's nice that you offered to have the sweater dry cleaned. Once it's returned, let's never trade clothes again. An experience like this last one is just too hard on both of us.

Major Writing Assignment

PERSUASIVE LETTER

So far in this chapter you have worked on these composition skills:

1. Backing up your ideas with reasons.
2. Using a business letter format.
3. Writing for different audiences.

Now it's time to put all of these things together in a new writing assignment. Your next paper will be a letter written to persuade (convince) the reader that your ideas make sense. Also, here's a chance to tell your teacher or principal (the audience) what you really would like to learn in school. Let's get started.

STAGE ONE: PREWRITING

Student Learning Objectives and Writing Prompt

In your letter you will:

1. write a **letter to your teacher** or **principal** which describes what you most want to learn and how you want to learn it.

2. use the first paragraph of your letter to tell **what you want to learn** and **why it's important**. (3 reasons)

3. use the second (and maybe third) paragraph of your letter to explain **how you would like to study or learn** the new material. (See **#4** on your **Think Sheet** for ideas.)

4. use a correct **business letter format** like the one found on **page 95**.

5. write only **complete sentences**.

6. write a letter which will convince **your audience**--your teacher or principal.

Name______________________________________

Think Sheet--Persuasive Letter

Before writing your letter you need to think about this topic. Answer these **think sheet questions** on your own paper. Later you can use the ideas to write a top-notch letter.

1. What is one thing you have really enjoyed doing in class or school in the last few years?

2. What was it about this lesson or unit that was the most fun for you?

3. What is your favorite subject in school? Why?

4. When you do work in your classroom, which of these things do you most like to do? Circle the **two** best.

a. Research to find new information in the library.
b. Work in groups with your friends.
c. Make things or build things.
d. Read by yourself.
e. Solve problems.
f. Work on art projects.
g. Give speeches.
h. Write stories, plays, or poems.
i. Put on plays.
j. Conduct science experiments.
k. Work on math problems.
l. Help another student your age or younger.
m. Work by yourself.

5. Look at the **two** items you circled above. Try to think of an example for each from your own days in school. Think of something you enjoyed. Describe it here.

6. In your free time, what things do you most like to do?

7. What's something you've always wanted to know more about?

8. What can a good teacher do to make learning fun?

9. Now it's time to look back over all your answers (**1-8**). Your next job is to use some of the information to begin to build your major ideas for your letter. Here's your idea outline.

A. In my class, I would really like to study:

____

____

B. To study this topic above, I would like to do the following activities or assignments:

____

____

C. My teacher could help me learn by:

____

____

D. To get a grade for my unit of study, I would complete or make what?

____

____

10. List at least three educational reasons why it would be good for you to study the topic you listed in **#9**.

____

____

____

STAGE TWO: WRITING THE FIRST DRAFT

Now it's time to draft your letter. Before you begin, be sure and check your learning objectives on **page 92**.

Helpful Drills

LETTER FORMAT

Your business letter needs to include these pieces. This is called the semi-block style.

1 Harbor View Road
sender's address---> Conklin, Nebraska 82116
date---> June 5, 1995

Mrs. R. White
New Haven Elementary
1160 Dear Park Rd. **<--- inside address**
Conklin, Nebraska 82116

Dear Mrs. White: **<---greeting with colon**

________________**Body with Paragraph Indents**________________
____
____
____

____
____
____
____

complimentary close---> Sincerely yours,

Elissa Emma Sagor

signature---> Signature

STAGE THREE: REWRITING

When your first draft is finished, you'll want to check it over and make improvements. To do this you might want to practice with the sample letter on the next page. Use the **editor's checklist** which follows the letter. Later you'll use the same **checklist** as you edit a partner's letter.

450 Moxie Road
Beau Monde, Washington 97773
May 5, 1995

Mr. Grover Parks, Principal
atilla Elementary school
14321 Sinclair Road
Beau Monde washington 97773

Dear Mr. Parks,

1. Thanks for taking your time to read this letter from one of yur students. **2.** Since I know that you work hard to make Atilla a good school. **3.** That's why Im writing. **4.** I just wanted some time to tell you that I think are fourth grade class could be made even better if we could spend two hole weeks studying whales, these wonderful sea creatures are truly remarkable. **5.** I have three very good reasons for this **6.** Most important, whales are interesting animal and some scientists think they may be extremely intelligent. **7.** Also, because we live near the ocean. **8.** So whales are something we cud study close at hand.

9. Our teacher, Ms. Zimus, is very creative and I know she could help us find some great ways to study and learn about whales. **10.** for example, I bet their are some great picture books in the liberry we could look through. **11.** The sea and huge whales could also be subjects for some exciting creative writing. **12.** But best of all, our hole class could go WHALE WATCHING! after we had learned about different kinds of whales. **13.** this would be a great reward for those students who had completed all their whale assigments.

14. Please think about these reasons for a whale unit and talk to Ms. Zimus if you agree with my ideas. **15.** Thanks so much for you time.

Sincerely,
Shelly Vincent
Shelly Vincent

Writer's Name________________________________ **Date**________

Editor's Name____

Editor's Checklist--Persuasive Letter

1. What is the topic the writer wants to learn about?

2. Does the writer list three (3) reasons why she wants to learn about the topic? What are they?

3. How does the writer want to learn about the topic? Is this clear?

4. What's the most convincing thing about this letter?

5. What one thing could the writer do to improve this letter?

6. Does the writer do anything special to make the principal like this letter? What?

7. Are there any errors in the date, inside address or greeting of the letter? What are they, if any?

8. Are there any sentence fragments which begin with a **glue word**? If yes, which numbers? Rewrite the sentences correctly.

9. Are any words misspelled? List them and spell correctly.

10. Can you find any punctuation errors? (Commas, periods, apostrophes?)

Sentence Opening Sheet

Before you move on to publish your letter, there is one more rewriting tip. It's called a **Sentence Opening Sheet** or **SOS** for short. An **SOS** asks you to fill out a chart like the one below. To fill out this chart, we used the sample letter you just edited on pages **90-91**.

First Three Words	# of Words	Good Vocabulary

Now you can look at the **SOS** chart and ask yourself some questions to help improve your letter.

First Three Words
(Write the first 3 words in each sentence.)

- Do any of the sentences begin with a **glue word** which means fragment alert?
- Is there a good mix of beginning words so that not all sentences sound the same way?
- Do all sentences begin with a capital letter?

# of Words
(Count the number of words in each sentence.)

- Is there a good blend of short and long sentences or are they all too much the same length?
- Are any sentences way too long?
  Could they be divided into two sentences?

Good Vocabulary Words
(Write down good vocabulary words used in each sentence.)

- Are there enough good vocabulary words?
- Which new vocabulary words could you add? Where?

Complete a **SOS** sheet like the one on the previous page for your own paper. Be sure to number each sentence before you start.

STAGE FOUR: PUBLISHING

When your entire class finishes all the letters, there will be some great ideas on paper. Your teacher may want to select five to ten of the most interesting ideas to be read aloud to the class. As a group you may want to vote to see which idea or ideas the class likes best. Who knows!! Your teacher may use some of the suggested ideas in her future lessons.

Stay Tuned

Maybe you have seen a copy of *People* magazine at the local grocery store. In the next chapter you'll be a reporter for *People.*

Writing an Article 5

What makes someone want to read a piece of writing? Think about yourself. Do you find that you keep reading stories or articles if they:

- tell you something that is interesting, exciting, or new

or

- use words and sentences in a fresh or creative way?

Good writers have to guess (or predict) what readers want to hear. In this chapter your job will be to create a magazine-like story which many people will want to read. You'll have to predict **what** the writer wants to read and **how** to write it. Your entire class will help with this project.

Oral Language into Writing

INTERVIEW TECHNIQUES

Newspaper reporters get a *scoop* when they write a *hot story* before anyone else does. To do this, they have to get information by asking many questions. This is called **interviewing**.

A topnotch interviewer must **predict** what others would want to know and then ask questions to find that information. Questions may fall into different topics or categories. Here's an example of an interview with a famous basketball player using a **question menu**:

QUESTION MENU: Famous Basketball Player

"The Game"	Social Life	Family	The Future	Special
Who was your best coach and why?	**How** do you relax off the court?	**How** many children do you have?	**When** do you think you'll stop playing?	**What's** the best thing you ever bought with all your money?
How do you prepare for a game?	**What** are the best and worst things about the place you live?	**Does** your wife ever travel with you out of town?	**How** are you preparing for life after basketball?	**Do** you think all pro athletes should graduate from college before they turn pro?
Which player is the toughest for you to guard?	**What** do you do in the "off" season?	**Are** your mom or dad athletes?	**Would** you live where you are if you didn't play basketball?	**What's** the hardest thing about your job? **What's** the best?
What does your team need most to improve?	**What** hobbies do you have?	**Are** any of your brothers or sisters also interested in basketball?	**What** do you want to be doing when you're 50?	**What** advice do you have for young players?
What game do you remember the most?		**Where** did you grow up?		
Who is the best player in the game?		**Why** did you start playing basketball?		

Oral Activity 1:

Below is a list of famous people. Working with a partner or in a small group, use a chart like the one in the example and write up a **Question Menu** for three (3) of the people from the list. Decide on the categories and the questions. Your first person must be the President of the United States, but you may choose the other two. You will be sharing your questions orally with the entire class.

PEOPLE

President of the United States
Queen of England
Babe Ruth
E.T.
any athlete/your choice
The Beatles
George Washington
Cochise
Hillary Clinton
Louis Armstrong
your great, great grandfather
Benito Juarez
a famous astronaut
Dr. Martin Luther King
Elvis Presley
Cesar Chavez
Abraham Lincoln
Christopher Columbus
Lewis & Clark
Joan of Arc
Eleanor Roosevelt

QUESTION MENU for____________________

Boxes for Categories			

Oral Activity 2:

Some stories are about actions or happenings and not just one person. To write about these stories, a reporter must ask a variety of questions and talk to many people. From the list of happenings (or events) below, choose two.

NEWSWORTHY EVENTS

A Strange Fire
A Bank Robbery
The Longest Baseball Game Ever Played
The Capture of Sasquatch
A Successful Brain Transplant
Finding a Five Pound Diamond
Someone Wins a Billion Dollar Lottery
The Loch Ness Monster is Photographed by Scientists
A Lady Who is 120 Years Old
Five Feet of Snow Falls in Florida
Mt. Rainier Explodes
Your Choice

With a partner, brainstorm all the questions you would need answered to write about each event. After you have listed as many questions as you think necessary, put your questions into groups. Lump together questions which have the same topic. Each of these groups can become a separate paragraph if you should decide to write about the event.

Simple Sentence Combining

ING WORDS

Good reporters are always searching for new sentence writing tips. A reporter who has used this book would know how to:

1. **expand** sentences with colorful words.
2. use compound sentences.
3. **combine** some sentences with **glue words**.
4. wipe out sentence fragments which start with a **glue word**.

Now it's time for one more idea. Look at this example.

Sentence Piece	Sentence Piece
Racing down the street.	The thief almost slammed into the wall.

New Sentence:

ING Phrase	Subject	Predicate
Racing down the street,	the thief	almost slammed into the wall.

The new sentence begins with an **ING** word--*racing*. The writer has hooked or glued this **ING** phrase to the main subject (**thief**) and predicate (**slammed**):

Many times, writers will use **ING** sentences to show action.

GLUING ING WORDS

Practice 1: Below are sentence pieces beginning with **ING words**. The other sentence pieces have subjects and predicates. Use your **writer's vocabulary** skill and **combine** any of the pieces in **Column 1** to any piece in **Column 2** and write five new sentences.

Example: *Slipping around the defender*, Bobo Grazinsky ended the game.

Column 1--ING Words

Crashing into the wall,
Whizzing past her teammates,
Slipping around the defender,
Roaring up the field,
Smiling into the defender's eyes,
Gliding effortlessly down the passing zone,

Column 2--Subject/Predicate

Bobo Grazinsky ended the game.
Greta knew her knee brace was doing its job.
the hockey player stunned the crowd.
the unknown player came out of nowhere.
the athlete looked like a ***Sports Illustrated*** cover photo.
the point guard heard the final buzzer ring.

When you have written the five sentences, try writing three (3) **ING** sentences with your own ideas. Share them with a partner or your group.

Practice 2: Use the **ING** phrases to glue on another part of the sentence. Complete the sentences below by **expanding** with a subject and predicate to the **ING** phrase. Be sure the sentences make sense. The first one has been done for you.

1. ***Slithering past the trap,*** the snake crawled into the tunnel.
2. Clutching her package,________________________________
3. Flying down the path,________________________________
4. Shrieking at the top of her lungs,________________________
5. Sighing softly,____________________________________
6. Struggling down the hall,______________________________
7. Jiggling like a crazy jellyfish,__________________________
8. Wiping a tear from her eye,____________________________
9. Soaring into the stadium,_____________________________
10. Bobbing on the calm sea,__________________________

Now try writing 6-8 **ING** sentences of your own.

An Easy Composing Rule

PUNCTUATING SENTENCES WITH ING PHRASES

You'll notice that in all the **ING** sentences you've written so far, a **comma** comes between the **ING** phrase and the rest of the sentence. In the sentence, you find the subject and the predicate which completes the sentence.

Crash**ing** through the hedge**,**	Luanda	grinned at everyone.
ING Phrase / **Comma**	**Subject**	**Predicate**

Note that ING sentences need a comma between the ING phrase and the rest of the sentence.

FRAGMENT ALERT!

It is also important to remember that a lonesome **ING** phrase by itself is just a **fragment**--not a complete sentence. This lonesome fragment will need another part of the sentence, with a subject and predicate, to make one complete sentence.

Running low on gas = lonesome **ING fragment**

Running low on gas, the old car finally came to a stop. = **sentence**

Practice 3: In the 15 examples on the next page, some of the sentences are complete. You just need to add the comma after the **ING** phrase and circle the comma. Write these sentences adding a comma where necessary. Other items are just lonesome **ING phrases**. Label these **fragment** or **frag** for short. Then **expand** each fragment into a complete sentence. The first two are done for you.

Remember your 3 x 5 ***I Believe That*** card from **Chapter 2**.

I Believe That

1. Whistling softly in the dark, the cop walked her beat.
2. Singing in the rain. **(FRAG)**
3. Racing like a missile past the moon. (**Tricky**)
4. Zipping out of the pocket the quarterback flicked the ball.
5. Groaning under the weight the scale read 305 lbs.
6. Inching across the table.
7. Begging for just a crust of bread or a penny.
8. Calling out for more pasta.
9. Sipping on her coffee she smiled up at him.
10. Hopping nervously down the path the bunny heard the footsteps.
11. Begging for mercy.
12. Rattling down the trail the pack horse woke up all the birds.
13. Singing in the shower my dad makes the soap cry.
14. Tearing up to the curb.
15. Gulping down her medicine the baby looked up with watery eyes.

WRITING FOR PUBLICATION

As we near the end of ***Flip the Deck***, it's time to use all your new writing skills. For this writing activity, you and your whole class will create a class magazine ready for publication.

Your publication will be a ***People*** magazine of sorts. It will feature real people from your school and community. Are you ready to become a published writer and author? The rest of this chapter will help you put all your skills together!

Helpful Practice Before Writing Your *Hot Scoop*

Before writing the first draft of your story, you need to learn a little about writing a news story. This kind of writing is called **journalistic** (jur na **lis** tik) **writing**. This is the kind of writing you find in newspapers and magazines. On TV, reporters also read journalistic or news stories aloud.

A reporter or news writer must give the reader new information. This means the writer must:

- cover all the facts
- grab the reader's attention
- answer the journalistic questions of **who**, **what**, **when**, **where**, **why**, and **how** early in the story

WRITING A LEAD

As you just read, a news story must cover key information early on. Readers are busy. They want to learn the important facts without having to read pages and pages. Therefore, a news story looks somewhat like this:

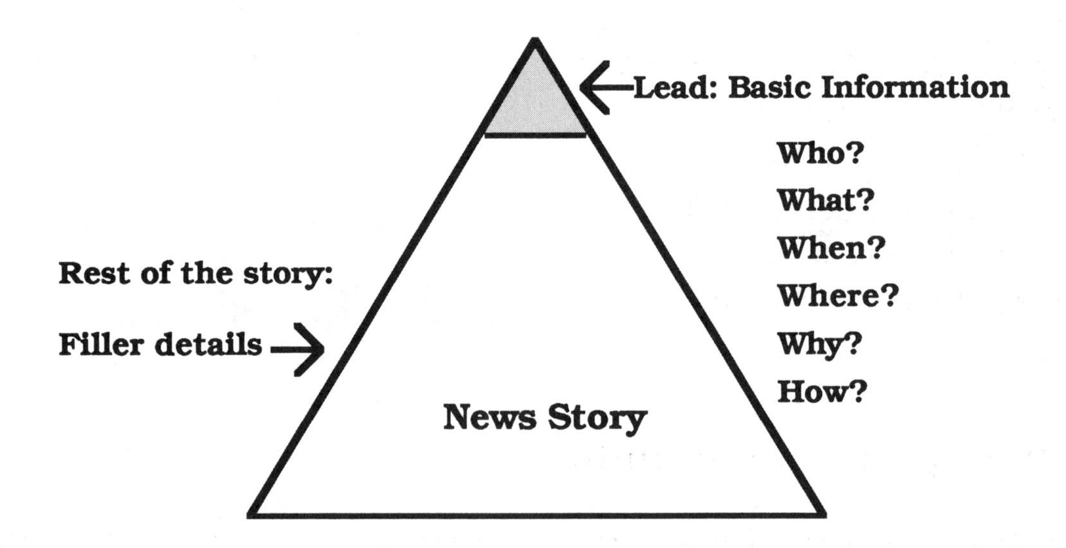

The basic facts of the story are covered early in the lead. Then, more slowly, the other details of the story are filled in to make a complete picture.

Hooking the Reader

When a reporter begins a news story, he/she needs to hook the reader quickly so that the **who**? **what**? **when**? **where**? **why**? and **how**? are known. There are many different ways to do this.

Here are a few:

- Make a surprising or startling statement related to the story.
- Ask the reader a question.
- Appeal to the reader's emotions.

Here are three samples of different leads about the same story. Notice how the reader is hooked and how the **who**? **what**? **when**? **where**? **why**? and **how**? get written quickly in the first paragraph.

Lead One: Surprising Statement

Megan lost 10 lbs. and five pairs of shoes, but she helped feed six families for a year. Last fall Megan McHaffee, a student at Glen Grove Elementary, sponsored and participated in three school dance marathons to help feed the hungry. Her efforts alone raised $4,500 dollars as she danced for 60 hours . . .

Lead Two: Question for the Reader

Would you ask for bleeding blisters, swollen feet, and leg cramps if you could feed a hungry child? Megan McHaffee certainly did. Last fall . . .

Lead Three: Emotion Appeal

Megan McHaffee hadn't slept for almost 24 hours, and she stumbled as she danced on and on. Sometimes she seemed to be dreaming even as she moved. In the dark, however, with the music blaring she saw in her mind the hungry three-year-old she had met at the shelter for the homeless. Last fall Megan McHaffee helped that child and many others as she danced for over 60 hours and raised $4,500 to feed the hungry.

Practice 4: Below is some **who**? **what**? **when**? **where**? **why**? and **how**? information for a story. Write three different leads using the same information. Feel free to make up more facts if you need them.

Who? A dog named Moses and a boy named Mark.

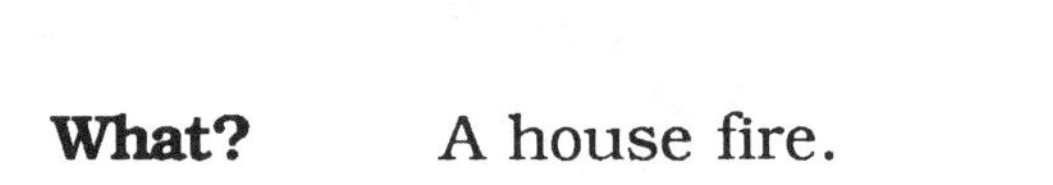

What? A house fire.

When? The fire occurred on Christmas Eve.

Where? The fire started in the living room with bad Christmas tree lights.

Why? Mark is alive today because his dog Moses crawled down a burning hall and woke him up by licking his face.

How? Both the boy and the dog escaped by climbing out the window and onto the porch roof.

Major Writing Assignment

WRITING AN ARTICLE

STAGE ONE: PREWRITING

Student Learning Objectives

In your news story you will:

1. write an article about an **interesting person** focusing on key information about that person for your audience.

2. write a **lead** which will hook the reader and move into **who**? **what**? **when**? **where**? **why**? and **how**? information.

3. use **adjectives, descriptive words, special vocabulary words**, **similes,** or **alliteration** to make your language fun to read.

4. write **compound, glue word,** and **ING sentences**. (At least 2 of each.)

5. write in complete sentences--no **fragments**.

6. write a **good title** for your story.

Writing Prompt

As a reporter your first job is to decide **who** to write about. Since your class magazine is about people, you will need to be sure to write about someone with an interesting story to tell. This could be a friend, a teacher, a relative, or someone who lives close by (even if you have never met them).

Remember, even ordinary people have remarkable stories to tell. It is your job to bring those stories to life. Talk with your teacher and at home with your parents. Think of two or three possible people to interview.

Ask yourself these questions to help narrow your choice.

- What do I already know about this person?

- Why would other people find my subject interesting?

- Will he or she be easy to talk to?

- Do I know someone else who can introduce me?

- What would I want to know if I were reading about this person?

- What special stories do they have to tell?

Practice 5: As you did earlier in this chapter, you need to complete a **QUESTION MENU** for your interview. Fill it out with good questions which will help you find interesting information. Use the model on the next page. You need to have at least four questions for each section. Look back to pages **103-104** to see how you did this before.

QUESTION MENU

My Name:____

I will interview:____________________________________

Question Categories or Topics

Topic One:	**Topic Two:**	**Topic Three:**	**Topic Four:**
__________	__________	__________	__________

Questions I Will Ask

For each topic or category you listed above, write at least three questions.

When you complete your **Question Menu** share it with your parents or teacher. They may have other suggestions to help you.

Next Step

Follow the steps on the **Hot Scoop Checklist** on the next page as you get ready to write your story. Be sure you have your teacher sign off on each step. You should have already completed the first three steps on this checklist. All the other writing aids you need are in this chapter.

HOT SCOOP CHECKLIST

	Date	Teacher Check
Helpful practice done: *Leads*	_____	_____
Interview person selected	_____	_____
Question Menu completed	_____	_____
Interview scheduled	_____	_____
Interview completed	_____	_____
Think Sheet done	_____	_____
First draft done	_____	_____
Draft read aloud to editing group	_____	_____
Revision Sheet filled out at home	_____	_____
Final draft done	_____	_____
Picture or art work done	_____	_____
Magazine goes to press	_____	_____

Name______________________________

Think Sheet--Class Magazine

Before you can finish the **Think Sheet**, you will need to conduct your interview. Your teacher will give you some advice about this.

Practice 6: (Please use your interview notes to help you as you complete this **Think Sheet**.)

1. What are the most important things you learned about the person you interviewed?

____

____

____

2. What surprising things did you learn?

____

____

____

3. Do you need some additional information to fill out your story?

____

____

____

4. What did you learn which could really grab a reader's attention? You might want to use this for the beginning of your story.

____

____

____

5. What extra information may not be all that useful in your story?

____

____

____

____

____

6. What facts or information will you want to be sure and mention in the story? Try to think of three main ideas which could become three main paragraphs.

Main Idea

A. ______________________________

____

____

Main Idea

B. ______________________________

____

____

Main Idea

C. ______________________________

____

____

For each main idea above, brainstorm some supporting details which you could use to round out a paragraph for each idea.

Idea One:____

____

____

____

Idea Two:____

____

____

____

Idea Three:______________________________________

____

____

____

7. Write two compound sentences which could be used in your story. Use information you learned in the interview.

____

____

8. Write two sentences about your person which begin with **glue words**. **(Chapter 2)**

____

____

9. Write two **ING** sentences which could be used to show action in your story.

10. ***Very Important**! List ten colorful words, action words, or special vocabulary words which could fit into your story. Think carefully about this and use a dictionary or thesaurus if you want.

11. Write a simile or an alliteration which would help the reader see something you want to describe.

STAGE TWO: WRITING THE FIRST DRAFT

Now it's time to write your first draft using your interview **Think Sheet**. Refer back to the objectives on **page 115** before you begin. You may want to write more than one lead before you choose the one you like best.

STAGE THREE: REWRITING

Reporters and authors always have editors who suggest changes in their original work before it goes to press. For this assignment, you will use two editing groups: classmates and adults at home or someone other than your teacher. You will work with a group of three or four classmates as a beginning step. Your classmates will use a **listener's response sheet** to help with this.

First-- Each person will read their story aloud (**quietly**) to the rest of the group.

Second-- Each person in the group will fill out a **listener's response** sheet after listening to the paper. Your teacher will give you extra copies. Each writer will attach these sheets to the back of his or her paper.

Third-- You will ask a parent/s or some adult other than your teacher to fill out the **editor's checklist**. This will go at the very back of your packet.

Writer's Nam

Listener's Na

Listener's Response Sheet

1. The things I liked about this news story are:

2. Your lead did/did not catch my attention. Here are my reasons why:

3. I have a question about or I did not understand . . .

4. My suggestion for improving your story is:

Writer's Name______________________________

Adult's Signature______________________________

Editor's Checklist

Please circle a score for each section of this news story based on your impression of the story. Remember that this is a first draft, so the story will have room for improvement. Please add comments and suggestions. The more you can provide, the greater the help to the writer. Thanks for your help.

1. *Angle* or Human Interest of the Story
Was the story interesting?

Yawn	**Hmmm**	**Super**
Fairly boring. Maybe you need a new angle. Back to the drawing board.	Some good passages. Basic story is OK. Some more detail would help.	Very interesting. I read it straight through. Learned a lot. Unique person.

1 2 3 4 5 6 7 8 9 10

Suggestions:______________________________

____

____

____

2. Lead into the Story
Did the opening sentences grab your attention?

Unexciting	**So-So**	**You Bet!**

1 2 3 4 5 6 7 8 9 10

Reasons for your score:______________________________

____

3. Use of Words and Descriptive Language
Did the words and phrases make this piece easier and more fun to read?

Snooze	**Average**	**The Golden Pencil Award**
Language is not colorful or different. Words seem to drone on and on.	Some good passages. More could be added.	Great vocabulary. Good use of adjectives, adverbs, similes, or alliteration. Very entertaining.

1 2 3 4 5 6 7 8 9 10

Examples I liked or suggestions:______________________________

____

4. Sentence Structure

Try Again
Many fragments.
All sentences seem the same.

So-So
Only one fragment.
Some good sentence beginnings, but needs more.

A #1!
No fragments.
Interesting sentence beginnings.

1 2 3 4 5 6 7 8 9 10

Examples or suggestions:____

____

5. Overall Rating

Needs Much Work

OK!

Terrific!

1 2 3 4 5 6 7 8 9 10

Comments:____

____

____

____

STAGE FOUR: PUBLISHING

Using all your response sheets, you will want to make corrections and write a final draft. This draft needs to show real changes and improvement from your rough draft.

Your class and teacher will work as an entire publishing group to put many stories together in one large ***People***-type magazine.

Your publishing group will need to decide on:

- Layout.
- Art work-- maybe a picture should go with each story. Photos?
- Size of the magazine.
- Book binding.
- How the book will be shared.

In the next chapter you will be an *adult* and write a memo as an employee of a corporation.

Writing on the Job 6

One reason to practice writing in school is that it helps prepare you for the time when you will write on the job. Whether you want to be a doctor, a farmer, a mechanic, a hair dresser, or an artist, almost any job will require you to do both *technical* reading, writing, and speaking.

This means that you must be able to read and communicate using information which is connected to all of the special parts of your job. In this chapter, you will have a chance to practice *technical*, real-life writing. It is never too early to brush up on these skills.

Oral Language into Writing

Oral Activity 1: Communicating for a Purpose

When you are communicating in a work setting, you are not writing or speaking to entertain or just to have fun. Instead, you are working to perform a specific task. You must be very clear about your purpose.

In addition, when you are working, you must often use your oral language and your written language skills together. The following activity will serve as a good warmup for some of the upcoming tasks in this chapter. Plan to work with a partner on this activity.

On the next pages are two imaginary situations. You and your partner are to choose just one of the situations. After reading the directions, you are to work together to write up some notes (on a separate sheet of paper or on some note cards) as you give a one to two minute oral presentation to your class.

Remember that you are *role-playing* and acting as if you are really the people in the situation.

Situation 1

The Scene: You and your partner have just made a new product--stamps and stamp pads which come in ten of the hottest new shapes. Kids can add their name or any other name to the stamp, personalizing each stamp on their own. In addition, the ink on the stamp pads comes in many colors, has sparkles in it, and glows in the dark.

Your Task: Your team has two minutes to make a presentation to the local PTA in order to convince them that selling the stamps and pads would be the best choice for the spring fund raiser.

The first speaker (one minute only) should introduce the product--the stamps--and explain their design, special features, cost, etc.

The second speaker (again only one minute) is to explain why this product will be a hot seller with other students and why it would make an excellent gift. This speaker also closes the presentation. Your biggest job is to be *persuasive!* You must turn in your notes after your presentation.

Situation 2

The Scene: You and your partner are co-chairs for the school talent show. Each year the talent show gets better because the organizers learn new ideas from watching the progress of last year's show.

This year, as co-chairs, you and your teammate want to use some very new ideas about how to advertise for the show and how to give student participants some tips to help them practice better. You also have some ideas about the type of acts that would make the show better.

Your Task: As the two co-chairs, you and your partner are meeting with your organizing committee. The first speaker (one minute only) is to make an introduction and explain his or her ideas about advertising for the show and tips for practicing for the show.

The second speaker (again, only one minute) will describe what kind of acts might be good for the show and also encourage the committee to make this the best show yet. This speaker also closes the presentation. Your biggest job is to *motivate!* You must turn in your notes after your presentation.

Simple Sentence Combining

Throughout ***Flip the Deck***, you have practiced several **writer's vocabulary** skills which can help make your writing seem stronger and more professional. Nowhere is this more important than when you are writing for a real purpose.

No matter what the job (or how old you are when you are working), an employee is constantly being evaluated by how he/she performs. This includes getting things done, getting along with other people, speaking and writing!

Practice 1: As an example, look at the letter that Seth wrote on the next page. Seth is the president of his class and must work with the parent committee to organize a big 5th grade fund-raiser. This fund-raiser will be a *three-on-three basketball tournament.* Mrs. Tuffnagle, the PTA president, has asked Seth to write a short letter to one of the local businesses to ask for some donations for prizes.

Read the letter and then follow the directions.

April 15, 1996

Mr. Rodney Rodbody
Mountain Man Sporting Goods Store
4415 Gecko Street
Camas, Washington 98607

Dear Mr. Rodbody:

1. Hello sir. **2.** how are you. **3.** My name is Seth Burk. **4.** I am 11 years old. **5.** Im in the fifth grade in Camas. **6.** I am class president. **7.** I am asking for help for a speshul project as part of my job. **8.** This is an important request. **9.** Because are class is having a fund raiser to buy new books for the liberry.

10. During a class meeting. **11.** we all got together and desyded to help the liberry. **12.** We thot a good way to do this would be to have a *three on three* basketball tournament. **13.** So far we've worked hard to organize this, now all the details are set. **14.** The tournament will be on Saturdar, May 15th, we hope you might be able to help. **15.** All of the students rilly like the things in yur store **16.** All of the students know you support the schools. **17.** We also thought that nice prizes wud help us attract more peeple to the fund raiser. **18.** This is where you come in.

19. If there are one or too items from your store. **20.** Perhaps you could donate these to our tournament. **21.** We are looking for basketballs t-shirts posters or hats. **22.** Almost anything you could provide would be great. **23.** We wud be sure to give you credit in our ads. **24.** If there is any merchundize you could spare. **25.** Please give me a call at home (834-1145) or at school (834-2811). **26.** Are class is anshus to here from you soon.

Sincerely,

Seth Burk

Seth Burk, 5th Grade Class President

By yourself or with a partner, reread the letter and decide how effective Seth has been at this task. Does the letter present his class request in the best way possible, or are there problems with the letter?

If you believe there are some glaring errors in the letter, see how many you can find. Using your proofreading symbols and a copy of the letter your teacher will give you, mark as many of the errors as you can find.

Practice 2: Next it is time to see if you can help rewrite Seth's letter so that it is really improved. For this, you should not only correct the spelling and punctuation errors in the letter, but you also need to use some of your **writer's vocabulary** sentence **combining** skills you know from this book.

These include:

1. using **glue words** to **combine** sentences or to add variety to your sentences,
2. getting rid of sentence **fragments** which start with **glue words**,
3. making some sentences compound sentences,
4. stretching some of your sentences by **expanding** with a few well-placed descriptive words,
5. checking to be sure that several sentences **do not all start** with the same word, and
6. using the **punctuation rules** you have learned.

Rewrite the letter on your own paper as you use all of the reminders above. Your teacher will share some sample letters from the class. Decide which *re-writes* Seth should send.

An Easy Composing Rule

SETTING OFF GLUE WORD CLAUSES--DEPENDENT CLAUSES

As writers grow and practice, they will find that they begin to write longer and more complex sentences. This is quite positive, and young writers should also be learning new punctuation rules which go along with these more advanced sentences.

In this chapter, you will pick up one more comma use tip. This is how to use a comma to set off a part of a sentence which begins with a **glue word** (a dependent clause).

You will remember from **Chapter 2** that writers often use **glue words** to begin sentences. Here are some of the original **glue words** you learned as well as some new **glue words**.

Possible Glue Words

after	although
as	because
before	if
since	though
until	unless
when	whenever
while	

Notice how some of the **glue words** (subordinating conjunctions) from the list above are used in the following sentences. They are in **bold**.

Example 1:

1. **Because** of the heavy rain, the worms are swarming over the driveway.

2. **Whenever** I go rollerblading down by the docks, I wear my purple streak helmet.

You will also notice that in these sentences there are two different parts of the sentence or clauses which **combine** to make the complete sentence. **Example 2** shows where the two clauses appear.

Example 2:

1. **If** I have to load that piece of software one more time, I will scream.
subject verb / subject verb
dependent clause 1 / dependent clause 2

2. **Until** I have trained my colt to use the bridle, I will have to use the halter.
subject verb / subject verb
dependent clause 1 / dependent clause 2

Clause

A clause is a group of related words that form a part of a sentence. As you can see above, a clause must also have its own subject and verb. However, some clauses cannot stand on their own to form a complete sentence. Instead, they depend on the rest of the sentence to make sense.

In the two sentences above, the first clause is dependent upon the second clause to make complete sentence sense. Notice that the dependent clause also begins with a **glue word**.

Important Comma Rule

When a dependent clause (starting with a glue word) comes at the beginning of a sentence, that clause must be set off with a comma. If a dependent clause beginning with a glue word comes at the end of a sentence, there is no need for a comma.

Example 3:

1. **Before** I was able to get my life saving certificate, I had to spend many hours in the pool. (comma necessary)

2. We will have strawberry pizza **unless** the anchovy sundaes are made first. (no comma necessary)

Practice 3: In the following sentences, underline the **glue word** and place commas where they are necessary.

1. Until you can afford the monthly fee you will have to wait to get Internet service.

2. Whenever I see Mathilda J. Snodgrass on top of the monkey bars I hear bells ringing and birds singing.

3. We go to the library almost every week because we love to read the *Baby-sitter's Club* books.

4. As the sun began its slow climb in the eastern sky I gradually sank farther and farther under the covers.

5. I've known Lester Mester since he was a pipsqueak holding his binky.

6. I think I will rent a movie and invite some friends over unless Bunny Phillips wants to go play road hockey.

7. Although it was a lovely, sunny day I couldn't find my new hiking sandals.

8. Before the deer have eaten all my mom's roses I think I'll put up some netting.

9. Herbie really likes that new software game although he thinks the graphics could be a bit better.

10. If you decide to take wind surfing lessons this August let me know if I could join you.

PRACTICE 4: The following note is missing several commas. Some are needed to set off dependent clauses while others are necessary to follow the other rules you learned earlier in the book. (See pages **13**, **38**, **60**, and **109**.)

There are 8 commas missing in all. On your paper list the number of each sentence including a missing comma. Behind the number write the word before and after the comma as well.

June 17, 1995

Iris,

1. Thanks for leaving me with the information about this year's softball candy
2. sale. I've heard that the prizes for top sellers are fun useful and easy to win
3. if you work hard. Although I'm not going to take over officially as president
4. until September I do want to learn how the fund raising works. I would like
5. to make enough to buy new duffel bags for the team but I don't want to
6. spend all of our time selling things. Our real job is hitting running and
7. scoring! Thanks again for dropping the packet by my house. When you get
8. back from hoop camp give me a call. We can go swimming.

See you soon

Janelle

Writing with Style

Professional writers often have important information to tell, and they need to make it easy for readers to follow along. If ideas or topics are scattered or jumbled, the reader can get confused or frustrated.

When you are writing about tasks on the job or if you are trying to tell someone how to do something, it is very important to be sure that one idea flows into another idea. In writing, this is called **unity**. All the ideas and topics need to be **unified** (tied together) in some way.

To help with this task, there are certain words or phrases that writers can often use to help relate one idea or paragraph to another. Notice how the **bold** words help to show this connection.

EXAMPLE 1:

1. We told the restaurant manager how much we had enjoyed the food. **In addition**, we filled out a comment card at the counter to thank the waitress.

2. We took the bikes off the car and attached the wheels. **Next**, we put on our helmets and filled our water bottles.

3. I liked that video we rented for many reasons. **For example**, it kept you on the edge of your seat during the car chase scenes.

Transition Words

These bold words are called **transitions** because they help you make a transition from one thought to another. They *bridge* ideas.

also	consequently
finally	first
for example	in addition
in conclusion	next
similarly	therefore

Transitions can be used to *join* the ideas in two sentences. They can also be used to join the topic sentence in a new paragraph to the previous paragraph.

Practice 5: The writer has used a memo form to send a message from her office to all the other employees on her staff. This type of memorandum or *memo* is often used on the job when ideas need to be communicated quickly.

The memo form is simpler and used when writing to one person or several. The *RE*: in the header of the memo stands for *REGARDING*. This is where the writer states the topic.

In this memo, the writer has used several transitions. Please circle the transition words or phrases on your copy of the memo and then finish the memo the way you think the writer would want it finished. In your part of the memo, use at least one transition of your own.

April 12, 1998

TO: ***Mascots and More*** Employees
FROM: Elsbeth Hempel, President
RE: Next Year's Products

Recently we decided to do some market research to help us decide which new products we should develop for next year. This spring, as in past years, we completed both phone and written surveys with our customers. Also, we tried something new this year and asked our employees for their thoughts. This was a very interesting process for several reasons. For example, we never realized that we would get so many ideas. Most of you gave us five or six suggestions!

In addition, the ideas were very creative and specific. Many of you pointed out that few schools order pelican suits or bulldog costumes any more. Instead you suggested that we continue to develop newer concept mascots like the *flames* or the *thunder*. We also got the message from you that buttons and ribbons are big sellers as spirit items for most schools.

In conclusion, all of this information has helped us come up with three or four new products for next year. Plan to see________________________________

____

____

____

____

Major Writing Assignment

ON THE JOB MEMO

STAGE ONE: PREWRITING

Student Learning Objectives

In this final assignment you will:

1. write an **on the job** memo using your best thinking about a problem to be solved at work.

2. use **language** and **ideas** which will best accomplish the purpose of the task.

3. use sentence **combining** skills to improve the variety of your sentences.

4. use **transition words** or phrases to connect your ideas.

5. write in complete sentences--no **fragments**.

Writing Prompt

Many times during a job you may have to put ideas in writing in order to accomplish a certain purpose. Sometimes you may need to communicate with many people at once. Other times you may be trying to persuade others to see your point of view or thoughts about something.

Often a written memo or letter is the easiest way to share information--especially so that others can refer back to facts they need to know. When you have to do this type of writing, it is important that you are clear about what your purpose should be.

In this **Major Writing Assignment**, you will be writing a business memo similar to the one on page **142**. Your job will be to tie together several pieces of information so that your memo is clear and solves a certain task.

In order to write this memo you need to know some important facts. Review the **Fact and Background Information Sheet**. After you have read this once, go back and decide how you would **combine** this information if you had to write a welcome memo for all the newspaper delivery students who worked for this newspaper.

As you read, make a mental note of the pieces of information which seem to be most important. After rereading the information, compare notes with a neighbor or partner and discuss what seems to be most important. Talk about what you say at the beginning of the memo, in the middle, and at the end.

Fact and Background Information Sheet

Who are you? Your name is Max Case and you are 13-years-old.

Where do you work? You work for the Kimberly Eagle newspaper chain and you have worked there for the past four years.

What's your job? You are the student trainer for all the other paper delivery persons. This includes 25 boys and girls ages 9 to 14. You deliver papers too, but also show the other kids how to best do the job.

Who is your boss? Wally Whitehead. He's the owner of the company.

Why were you hired for this job? You were hired for this job because you have always been on time, done your best, and can explain things easily to other students.

What are some key ideas, tips, or pieces of information you know about as a result of your job?

Item 1
On rainy days all papers need to be stuffed in plastic bags.

Item 2
It takes about three days to really learn your paper route.

Item 3
Mr. Whitehead really gets cranky when he gets complaints about missing papers from customers.

Item 4
Mr. Whitehead likes for all questions from delivery people to be routed to you instead of the office. He likes for problems to get taken care of somewhere else.

Item 5
It's OK for either bikes or cars (with parent drivers) to be used to deliver papers as long as the papers get delivered on time.

Item 6
Mr. Whitehead likes for all his delivery people to wear their Kimberly Eagle T-shirts as much as possible when delivering the papers.

Item 7
If you get sick and can't do your route, please call 733-2699 as soon as possible to arrange for a substitute.

Item 8
There will be a meeting for all new delivery students at 10:00 on Saturday morning June 1, 1999. It will be held at the Community Center.

Item 9
When customers call Mr. Whitehead to compliment a friendly or helpful delivery person, he loves it.

Item 10
This is a great job with good pay for kids who have a good attitude.

Name____

Think Sheet--On the Job Memo

As you can see from the memo, Max has lots of information rumbling through his head. His job is to sort it all out so that he can write a clear memo to the new workers at the paper. See if you can help to sort out the information so that it is organized by categories.

1. Jot down ideas from the sheet and organize them under each heading.

General Rules

Special Tips to Get Ahead

Information Only Max Needs to Know

Facts the Employees Will Need for the Future

2. If you were to receive a welcome memo from Max as a new employee, how would you like it to read? List some brief descriptive words or phrases to explain how you think the memo should *sound*.

3. Assume that there will be three paragraphs in this memo. List the major topics or ideas you will cover in each paragraph using the organizer below.

Paragraph #1 Main Idea____

Supporting Examples or Details:

____

____

____

Paragraph #2 Main Idea____

Supporting Examples or Details:

____

____

____

Paragraph #3 Main Idea____

Supporting Examples or Details:

____

____

____

4. How will you write the header for the memo? Brainstorm some thoughts here. Do two examples and see which one you like the best.

TO:	TO:
FROM:	FROM:
RE:	RE:

STAGE TWO: WRITING THE FIRST DRAFT

By using the information from the fact sheet and also your **Think Sheet**, you should be ready to begin the first draft of your memo. Remember that you are writing as if you are Max. Your purpose is to make each new paper delivery person feel welcome. You also need to cover some important information in this first memo they receive from you.

When you write a **sloppy copy**, it is not perfect.

- Guess how to spell hard words. Circle them to check later. Then go on. **Guess and Go**.
- Write quickly to keep your ideas flowing. Handwriting does not have to be your neatest at this time.
- Work on the story later. Not all parts must be perfect.

To make your memo easier to work on later:

- Write in pencil.
- Skip every other line.
- When you finish, go back and number each sentence you wrote.

STAGE THREE: REWRITING

As you learned earlier, it is even more important to be sure that your written work on the job is done well. This is because it is often read by many people and because your own performance can be judged by what you say. Now that it is time to polish up your memo, use a favorite revision tip to make your final draft the best possible.

When revising, it is always a good idea to use a tool like the **Sentence Opening Sheet** which you first used on page **99**. Complete an SOS sheet like the on the next page using the sentences from your own memo and your own paper.

Name____

Sentence Opening Sheet

First Three Words Per Sentence	# of Words	Power Words

Now you can look at the chart and ask yourself some questions to help improve your letter.

First Three Words

(Write the first 3 words in each sentence.)

- Do any of the sentences begin with a **glue word** which means fragment alert?
- Is there a good mix of beginning words so that not all sentences sound the same way?
- Do all sentences begin with a capital letter?
- Do some of the sentences begin with transitions in order to help the ideas connect?

# of Words

(Count the number of words in each sentence.)

- Is there a good blend of short and long sentences or are they all too much the same length?
- Are any sentences way too long?
  Could they be divided into two sentences?

Power Words

Power words are well chosen vocabulary words that show that you can use more mature vocabulary and words that are a little more challenging. Look through your memo and find some dull ordinary words which could be improved. Using the thesaurus or your own ideas, replace the common place words (make at least a couple of changes) with a more grown up choice.

- List your new vocabulary words after you have made the change.
- Which other vocabulary words do you feel you used well?

STAGE FOUR: PUBLISHING

Take home your draft and **Sentence Opening Sheet**. Share both of these with your parents or another adult friend. Ask them for some ideas to help make your final memo very strong. Look for suggestions they might have about how work related memos should sound.

When you have this feedback, you will be ready to write your final draft. Be sure you do this on a clean sheet of paper using your very best handwriting. If you are lucky enough to be able to use a word processor, this would be a good assignment to type.

When your class has finished all their final memos, it might be a good idea to give them all to your principal. Ask her (or him) to look them over and to pull out of couple of examples which she or he feels are good examples of employee work. Invite the principal to share these samples, her ideas and her other thoughts about writing on the job with your entire class. No doubt she'll see what a class act you all are!

Student Objectives and Evaluation Sheets--Grading Sheets

Name____

Chapter 1--Description Scoring Guide

IDEAS	SENTENCES	CAREFUL WRITING
50 points	**30 points**	**20 points**
Fun to read! Action moves quickly! The writer's imagination is original and there are unexpected neat surprises. A real page turner!	All sentences begin with a capital and have ending punctuation. They describe one main idea. Good similes which help make the action or things easy to see. Good colorful words. Expanded most sentences.	Handwriting is neat and readable. Correct use of commas in a series. No spelling errors.
30 points	**15 points**	**12 points**
Many of the descriptions and actions are fun to read. Some new vocabulary words or ideas could be added to spark things up. Some parts are a little boring or too much the same.	Similes need work. Are there two? Check for capitalization or ending punctuation errors in sentences. Some sentences could be spiced up with better colorful words and new information.	Handwriting is a little too sloppy. Check use of comma rule. Some spelling errors.
15 points	**8 points**	**5 points**
Ideas really need a a lot of work. Try harder to keep reader's interest. Needs more action and description. Work on adding more creativity.	Little use of similes. Sentences are choppy and need more work. Describe with better vocabulary. Some sentences need more expansion.	Paper is hard to read! Many spelling and punctuation. errors.

TOTAL POINTS: ____________ **TOTAL POINTS:** ____________ **TOTAL POINTS:** ____________

Comments:

Name____

Chapter 3--Creating a New Invention Grading Sheet

1. Use of Descriptive Language

Blah	**OK**	**Wow!**
Too many boring words.	Some interesting words and phrases.	Great adjectives. Good similes. Fun alliteration.

1 2 3 4 5 6 7 8 9 10

2. Creativity

Give Me a Break!	**Average**	**Oh Boy!**
I know you can do better than this. Way too ordinary.	Some good ideas- needs more.	Great imagination. Fun to read your ideas. Lots of extras. Wish I had thought of these.

1 2 3 4 5 6 7 8 9 10

3. Organization

Too Confusing	**Pretty Good**	**A Snap to Read**
Hard to follow. No clear flow.	Some jumping around.	Each paragraph a separate topic; easy to follow. Very well organized.

1 2 3 4 5 6 7 8 9 10

4. Sentence Structure

Try Again!	**So-So**	**Superstar!**
Many fragments. All sentences are the same length. Few, if any, compound sentences.	One fragment or not enough sentence interest. Few compound sentences.	No Fragments. Three compound sentences--all with commas.

1 2 3 4 5 6 7 8 9 10

5. Overall Impression

Back to the Drawing Board	**OK**	**Love It!**

1 2 3 4 5 6 7 8 9 10

Name____

Chapter 4--Persuasive Letter Grading Sheet

Your letter will be graded using this scale. Read this carefully, so you will know what to aim for as you write.

Ideas	Business Letter Format	Sentence Structure	Careful Writing
40 points	**20 points**	**20 points**	**20 points**
Learning ideas are clear and interesting. Three good reasons to support the main ideas. The letter would convince its reader.	Letter includes: date, inside address, greeting, paragraph indents, closing, and signature.	There are no fragments in this letter.	There is one or less spelling errors. All sentences begin with a capital letter and end with proper punctuation.
20 points	**10 points**	**10 points**	**10 points**
The main learning theme is clear, but reasons to support it are not clear.	Writer made one mistake in business letter format.	There is no more than one fragment in the letter.	There are 2--3 spelling, capitalization, or punctuation errors. Paper could be neater.
5-10 points	**5 points**	**5 points**	**5 points**
Ideas in the letter are not very interesting and are hard to follow. This letter would not impress a teacher or principal.	Business letter format is poor.	There are 2 or more fragments in this letter.	There are many errors in spelling, punctuation, or capitalization.

Name____

Chapter 5--Writing an Article for *People* Magazine Grading Sheet

1. *Angle* or Human Interest of the Story
Was the story interesting?

Yawn
Fairly boring.
Maybe you need a new angle. Back to the drawing board.

Hmmm
Some good passages.
Basic story is OK.
Some more detail would help.

Super
Very interesting.
I read it straight through. Learned a lot. Unique person.

10 15 20 25 30

2. Lead into the Story
Did the opening sentences grab your attention?

Quick Turn Off

So-So

You Bet!

10 15 20 25 30

3. Use of Descriptive Words and Language

Did the words and phrases make this piece easier and more fun to read?

Snooze

Language is not colorful or different. Words seem to drone on and on.

Average

Some good passages. More could be added.

The Golden Pencil Award

Great vocabulary. Good use of adjectives, adverbs, similes, or alliteration. Very entertaining.

5 10 15 20

4. Sentence Structure

Try Again!

Many fragments. All sentences seem the same.

So-So

Only one fragment. Some good sentence beginnings, but needs more.

A #1!

No fragments. Interesting sentence beginnings.

1 2 3 4 5 6 7 8 9 10

5. Overall Rating

Needs Much Work

OK!

Terrific!

1 2 3 4 5 6 7 8 9 10

Name____

Chapter 6--On the Job Memo Grading Sheet

1. Accomplishing a Purpose

Did this memo accomplish its purpose of informing the employees and helping them to do a better job?

Not Ready for Prime Time	**OK**	**Terrific**
Doesn't give the greatest first impression. Missing or confusing information.	Most key information included. Could be more polished.	Reads like it was written by a pro.

10 **15** **20** **25** **30**

2. Organization

Was the information organized so that it was easy for the reader to follow the writer's ideas?

Needs Lots of Help	**Getting There**	**Right on Target**
Jumps around too much. Missing Information. No use of transitions.	Fairly easy to follow. Some use of transitions.	Information is well organized. Transitions well used.

10 **15** **20** **25** **30**

3. Sentence Variety

Are there several different sentence beginnings in the memo? Do the sentences flow with a good rhythm?

Doesn't Make Sentence Sense	**Average**	**Outstanding**
Sentences are all too much alike. May contain sentence structure errors.	Some interesting sentences. Could use more work, however.	All sentences flow smoothly and lots of variety included.

10 **15** **20** **25** **30**